TO BUILD A CANAL

Miami University, through an arrangement with the Ohio State University Press initiated in 1975, publishes works of original scholarship, fiction, and poetry. The responsibility for receiving and reviewing manuscripts is invested in an Editorial Board comprised of Miami University faculty.

TO BUILD A CANAL

Sault Ste. Marie, 1853–1854 and After

BY JOHN N. DICKINSON

Published for Miami University
By the Ohio State University Press

Library of Congress Cataloguing in Publication Data

Dickinson, John N
To build a canal
Bibliography: p.
Includes index.
1. Sault Sainte Marie Canal—History. I. Title.
TC625.S2D53   386'.47'0977491   80-27693
ISBN 0-8142-0309-4

TO MARJORIE

Contents

Illustrations

Maps

Foreword

As in the affairs of men, there is an element of chance in the natural geography of our earth that can be favorable, or fatal, or merely adverse to man's use of his environment. Geologic chance surrounded Lake Superior with immense and valuable forests and placed near its shores rich lodes of copper and the world's largest and most accessible iron ore deposit, in the famed Mesabi Range. In the modern era a once unlikely resource, billions of tons of granitic rock yielding tiny particles of embedded iron, has given rise to the multibillion-dollar business of taconite extraction, now basic to the steel economy of Canada and the United States.

A quirk of geology and geography caused Lake Superior to have an elevation twenty-one feet higher than the level of Lake Huron, into which Superior flows. The two lakes are connected by the St. Mary's River. Another accident of nature caused this river not to flow by a gradual gradient over its sixty-three mile length (or seventy-five miles by the longest measurement of another channel). The drop occurs in a precipitous rapids, in a stretch of water only three-fourths of a mile long and a quarter of a mile wide, where the 74,000 cubic feet per second flow of Lake Superior hurtles toward Lake Huron in a welter of rock ledges and turbulent water that no canoe or ship could traverse.

These quirks of geology, geography, and hydrology have had enormous political, economic, and engineering consequences, which in turn led to the writing of this treatise by Dr. John N. Dickinson, whose research has added much to the literature of the phenomenon of Sault Ste. Marie.

The early French explorers called the connecting river between the lakes St. Mary's River (Ste. Marie in French). What we call the falls or rapids of the St. Mary's River the French identified as "Sault

Ste. Marie." The literal translation of the French word *sault* is *jump*; thus did the French fur traders identify the need for their early flotillas of canoes or bateaux to make the "jump" up and over (or down and over) the stretch of white water that neither they nor the Indians could overcome except by portaging around it.

As the French trade routes became established, reaching from Lake Superior and western Canada all the way back to Montreal, the early Jesuits devised a timber flume to facilitate the dragging of boats and cargo around the white water of the Sault. In 1797 the North West Company, trade concessionaire for the region, built the first lock on the Canadian side of the rapids. It was thirty-eight feet long and nine feet wide, and had a lift of nine feet and a draft of thirty inches. It served for seventeen years, until destroyed by American troops in 1814 on one of the American incursions of the War of 1812. This lock, which disappeared, was not rebuilt; and its foundations were not rediscovered until 1889, seventy-five years later.

After 1814 the portage process around the Sault Ste. Marie rapids had to be resumed if Lake Superior was to be linked with the other four lakes. In 1825 the opening of the Erie Canal brought flood tides of settlers and immigrants over the lakes to the rich new territories of Michigan, Illinois, Wisconsin, and Minnesota. In addition to wheat, timber, and furs, rich lodes of copper and iron had been located in the Superior region. With trade and population blossoming, and with Lakes Erie, Huron, and Michigan burgeoning economically, Lake Superior still lay inaccessible, twenty-one feet higher than Huron and with no solution to that three-quarter-mile stretch of white water.

Steam vessels succeeded the canoe and the bateau and began to overtake the schooner. In 1827 the first steamer, the *Henry Clay*, reached the St. Mary's River but could go no farther. Aboard it were General Lewis Cass, soon to be governor of Michigan, and General Winfield Scott, later to achieve fame as "Old Fuss and Feathers" in the war with Mexico and as chief of staff of the U. S. Army at the beginning of the Civil War. They were en route to inspect the forts west of Lake Michigan. Cargo from the *Clay*, and from other ships of the era, was unloaded and portaged around the rapids to the ships available for Lake Superior navigation.

With the phenomenal success of the Erie Canal and the

blossoming of the new western territories, there developed a classic case in the history of American political confrontations. As in the recent example of the St. Lawrence Seaway, the eastern "establishment" of ports and trade centers feared loss of population as well as economic competition from the new territories. Plank roads and canals were wanted everywhere in this prerailroad era, and federal aid was sought as avidly then as now.

For several decades the "Doctrine of Internal Improvements" was the battleground in Congress between East and West. It was finally resolved when Congress began to appropriate monies to improve the harbors of pioneer cities on the lakes and to grant lands as well as money for a variety of public improvements. The craze for local canals and plank roads collapsed as rails reached the West in the 1850s.

A towering figure on the federal political scene for decades was Henry Clay (1777–1852). Lawyer and professor, he became Speaker of the House and a several-time candidate for president, but achieved his greatest fame as U. S. senator from Kentucky. A principal architect of the Missouri Compromise, he is identified as "The Great Compromiser." However, he could be singularly uncompromising. As a leading "War Hawk," he was instrumental in forcing war with Great Britain in 1812, and boasted that the militia forces of Kentucky could conquer Canada by themselves.

In 1837 Governor S. T. Mason of the newly admitted state of Michigan urged his new legislature to approve a passage for ships around the falls of the St. Mary's River. Since the new frontier state had meager resources, it sought federal assistance, and the proposed locks and canal became a subject of congressional debate.

As a westerner, Clay generally supported "internal improvements," but he took a strong stand against the Michigan canal project. Apparently not impressed that the first steamer to reach the St. Mary's River had borne his name, in 1840 he rose to new heights of uncompromising opposition when he described the proposed lock and canal as "a work beyond the remotest settlement of the United States, if not the moon." Another great western American, Senator Thomas Hart Benton of Missouri, rebutted Clay by stating that the object was "not just a good one, but a great one." Clay's memory is tarnished by his lack of vision, and his quote about the moon is a landmark in the literature of the lakes. The canal he opposed so vehemently became within a single generation the world's busiest ship canal.

President Millard Fillmore in 1852 signed a federal authorization bill calling for a canal at least 100 feet wide and 12 feet deep, with a lock or locks at least 250 feet long and 60 feet wide. Given the ship sizes of that era, these were reasonably imaginative dimensions. Details of the bill are not at hand, but apparently it had been agreed that the state would build the canal through its Canal Commission. The state's vision was broader, and its action called for lock sizes not less than 350 by 70 feet.

Whatever the politics may have been, the right man appeared at the critical moment. A Fairbanks Scales salesman, Charles T. Harvey, helped form the St. Mary's Falls Ship Canal Company, which received the contract from the Michigan government. Harvey had seen with frustration the ships from Lake Superior unloaded, their cargoes portaged and laboriously reloaded into schooners and steamers, and all commerce frustrated by a short space of white water. The "Harvey locks" have been the principal interest of Dr. Dickinson, as evidenced by this new book.

The first iron ore cargo from Lake Superior passed through in the trim brigantine *Columbia* on 14 August 1855, consigned to Cleveland-Cliffs Iron Company, which to this day continues to remove Superior ore. The steamer S.S. *Illinois* was the first vessel into the locks on 18 June 1855.

Originally a toll canal (at four cents per ton), the Sault continued under state ownership and operation until 1881. By then it was clear that the route was of national importance and that the state probably could not finance needed expansion. Title was conveyed to the United States government, and Congress assigned jurisdiction to the Corps of Engineers on a toll-free basis. New and larger locks were successively completed in 1881, 1896, 1914, 1919, 1943, and 1969. The original state locks were removed. In 1895 the Canadian lock, 900 feet long, was built on the north side of the rapids. Less than 17 feet deep, it has had limited use, and the American locks and canal have served the bulk of the commerce.

In World War II the Sault locks were aptly described as "the jugular vein of the Allied War effort." More than 100 million tons of iron ore per year poured from the Mesabi Range eastward and southward to steel mills and factories producing the ships, trucks, aircraft, and supplies that were to defeat the Axis powers. The war efforts of Canada and the United States, and the gigantic lend-lease aid to allies, were based upon steel production. At one period, unknown to the public, the Sault Ste. Marie area was the most heavily defended spot in North America. New fighter airfields were built; many batteries of the most modern anti-aircraft artillery were stationed; and flotillas of barrage balloons floated over the Sault as they did over London. The fear was that Germany might develop a long-range bomber to penetrate the region and to blast the locks out of service.

Another giant effort was the building of the MacArthur lock under forced draft conditions, at the height of the war, to increase and enhance the vital iron ore flow. Completed in 1943, it was 800 feet long, 80 feet wide, and 31 feet deep, substantially the same as the Welland locks and future Seaway locks.

In 1969 the completion of a new Poe Lock, 1,200 feet long, 110 feet wide, and 32 feet deep, gave birth to the newest economic and transport phenomenon of the lakes—the thousand-foot bulk carrier. Landlocked in the upper four lakes and too large to transit Welland or Seaway locks, a growing fleet of these fresh-water leviathans is reshaping the economics and the hardware of lake shipping. Proposals for larger and deeper locks to accommodate even larger lake vessels have been advanced and are being studied.

Primarily serving the basic bulk cargo flows of the lakes region— ore, grain, coal, stone, and oil—the Sault waterway is also reflective of other trade routes. For example, in 1975, a year of moderate volume, it served 63.4 million tons of domestic Great Lakes cargo, over 8.6 million tons of cargo to and from Canada, and nearly 3.0 million tons of Seaway shipping, for a grand total of 75.2 million tons. There were 146,000 passengers by water, and 3,774 ships were locked through. The ships were fewer and larger—1,700 of them had drafts of twenty-six feet or more.

A waterways convention held at Sault Ste. Marie in 1887 noted that the building of the Suez Canal had cost $92 million; that the Sault canals had cost little more than $3 million; and that "Soo [sic] was serving a larger commerce than Suez." When the Sault tonnages began to pass the 100-million-ton mark per year, it was frequently boasted that the Sault handled more tons of commerce in given years than the Panama, Suez, and Kiel canals combined. In 1953 a record 128 million tons of ore, coal, grain, and other traffic used the Sault locks and canal. For the ten years 1945–54, tonnage averaged 107,300,000 tons per year, or over a billion tons in a decade.

The richest agricultural and industrial region of the world and a huge concentration of people are found in and around the Great Lakes. Ships from the oceans are lifted 602 feet from sea level to Lake Superior by the vast engineering works of the St. Lawrence Seaway, the Welland Canal, and the Sault locks. Of that tremendous lift, only 21 feet are accomplished at Sault Ste. Marie, but this is one of the most crucial small measurements in global history and in the economics of a continent. To the original builders, and to all the later engineers or navigators who enlarged upon their phenomenal achievement, the people of Canada and the United States, and even of the world, must be profoundly grateful.

HARRY C. BROCKEL
Center for Great Lakes Studies
University of Wisconsin—Milwaukee

Preface

It would be hard to exaggerate the economic importance of the St. Mary's Falls Canal, through which the vast mineral resources of the Lake Superior country move to mills and furnaces on the lower lakes. Linked to the coal and limestone of Ohio and Pennsylvania, these resources energized an industrial development undreamed of before the Civil War. From a nation with a multiplicity of small enterprises in 1860, an industrial giant would grow. It is strange, therefore, that there has not been a complete history of the construction of this important canal.

The only scholarly works published to date and devoted exclusively to the canal are an article and a book chapter by the Indiana University historian Irene D. Neu. Dr. Neu began her work in this field with her Cornell University dissertation, "A Business Biography of Erastus Corning," which she subsequently expanded into a book, *Erastus Corning, Merchant and Financier, 1794–1872* (Ithica: Cornell University Press, 1960). Her article, "The Building of the Sault Canal: 1852–1855," was published in the *Journal of American History* 40 (June 1953), and is far from comprehensive. Her book chapter, in *The Frontier in American Development: Essays in Honor of Paul Wallace Gates* (Ithaca: Cornell University Press, 1969), is primarily concerned with the disposition of the Michigan mineral lands owned by the Canal Company. A Michigan state senator, Otto Fowle, set out to write the entire history of the Sault area but died before he could complete the story of the canal. Another history, published in *Joint Documents of the State of Michigan* in 1887, is incomplete and filled with errors.

A number of questions should be asked. How was the canal a part of a vast number of engineering and commercial undertakings essential to the development of the American economy? What were the interactions between the forces interested in seeing a canal built and the rest of the country? What was the nature of the pressure brought upon Congress for the authorization of the canal? What were the relations among federal and state governments and private corporations during the building process? Who actually had the responsibility for the design and construction of the canal? Was the work honestly done? Were there any significant innovations in design? How was the project financed? What were the rewards to the contracting party?

No place on earth, including Michilimackinac, has had more forms and combinations of spellings than has the Sault. The citizens of the area dislike "Soo," even though a railroad has adopted that name. They dislike even more the sex transformation to "Sault St. Marie." "St. Mary" is correct for the river, and it is proper to speak of the "rapids of the St. Mary's River." However, it is just as incorrect to write of the "rapids of Sault Ste. Marie" as it is to write of the "Rio Grande River" or "Bull Run Creek." The characters of my story make all these mistakes and more. I have chosen to use their own terms and not to clutter the text with "*sics*."

I have used the old-fashioned term *rail road* to indicate rails spiked to a plank road with animals furnishing the power. The term *railroad* is used in the modern sense.

All survey ranges cited in the text are indexed to the Michigan prime meridian, which by happy coincidence runs through Sault Ste. Marie. Thus the reader can estimate the approximate distance in miles east or west of the canal by multiplying the range number by six.

I wish to express my appreciation to a Miami University colleague, Professor John L. Thompson of the Department of Geography, who aided in the presentation of the cartographic material. The manuscript was prepared through grants from the Miami University Faculty Research Committee and the Miami University Office of Development.

TO BUILD A CANAL

1 The Years of Frustration 1839–1850

Of the five Great Lakes, all but one have retained their Indian names. The exception is the largest, which the French explorers called simply Lake Superior—the *upper lake*. It is "upper" in the sense of being farthest north as well as in having an elevation approximately twenty-two feet above that of Lakes Huron and Michigan. Most of the twenty-two-foot fall occurs in one mile of the forty-mile course of the St. Mary's River, and it is estimated that some five million cubic feet of water flow past Sault Ste. Marie every minute. A formidable barrier it would be, effectively isolating the upper lake, were it not for the famous canal and locks that constitute the vital link.

Eighteenth-century traders first recognized the need, and a Sault canal—of sorts—was already in operation in the days of George Washington. Its builder, Scottish trader Simon McTavish, had formed the North West Company in 1783 to deal in furs, and the company maintained a post on the American side of the St. Mary's River. After the American Revolution, McTavish crossed the river and built his canal in 1797. It was little more than a ditch with a diminutive lock, but it served the canoes and bateaux of the North West Company for many years until its destruction in 1814 by an armed band of Americans. Its very existence was then forgotten for over seventy years until it was rediscovered in 1889. By then, however, canal builders of broader vision and greater means had come to Michigan.[1]

No account of the building of the Sault canal can begin without brief reference to the still-changing geology of the Great Lakes. The present form of Lake Superior probably developed about 2,300

Fig. 1. Replica of North West Company lock. Reproduced from the collections of the Michigan Department of State, State Archives.

years ago; before that time Lakes Superior, Michigan, and Huron were on the same level. A constant process of uplift subsequently raised the outlet of Lake Superior about six feet, while at the same time the Detroit River found a new and more easily eroded channel permitting a greater flow out of Lake Huron and Lake Michigan and so lowering the level of both about sixteen feet.[2]

The geology of the Sault area is more difficult to describe, primarily because geologists usually indicate the St. Mary's River as the southern limit of the great Canadian granite shield. The eminent geologist Charles Van Hise thought that the boundary occurred five miles north of the river. The surface of the shield descends beneath the soft sandstone deposits of the glacial age, a fact of great importance for a canal builder intending to excavate in the area. Whereas the sandstone would be easy enough to remove, the granite underneath it would present a much more serious and expensive problem. This information was available to the canal diggers of the 1850s; the annual report of the Michigan state geologist in 1841 noted the extent of red sandstone in the Sault area and warned that it rested on primary rock. Unfortunately the warning was not heeded by the impatient builders of the Sault canal.[3]

The Superior District was a wild and desolate place when Michigan obtained statehood in 1837. The lake itself deserved the description attributed to La Hontan—"an ocean in a storm, sculptured in granite." Inaccessible though the area was, its resources were not unknown, and in 1839 Michigan made plans to build a canal and petitioned Congress for a grant of either cash or land to aid the project. A select committee of the Michigan House of Representatives advised that the time was ripe to build and suggested that the job should be completed in one summer, since it would be too expensive to keep a labor force at the Sault through the winter. At the same time the Michigan Senate made an invidious comparison with federal grants made to Ohio for internal improvements: Ohio had received 1,511,555 acres, and Michigan only 124,800. The petition to Congress also cited the economic loss that the nation would presumably suffer if a canal were not built at Sault Ste. Marie.[4]

If the petition failed, Michigan was prepared to build the canal as a state project. In the summer of 1837, John Almy, a Michigan engineer, traveled to the Sault at the request of the legislature to see what could be done. Almy had some minor experience in Michigan canal work. In 1835 he had designed the canal and lock around the falls of the Grand River, a project about one mile in length with a drop of three feet. At the Sault, Almy proposed to build three locks, each 100 feet long and 32 feet wide. There would be a basin for ships to pass between each pair of locks. The canal itself would be 75 feet wide and 10 feet deep. Almy estimated that the cost of building such a canal would be $112,544. With Almy's report in hand, the Michigan legislature appropriated $25,000 to begin construction.

In September of 1838 the Buffalo firm of Smith and Driggs entered into a contract with the state to construct a canal, the work to commence the next year. Almy became chief engineer on the River Improvements and Sault Ste. Marie Canal Project, as it was called, and it seemed that Michigan would at least make a start toward eliminating the impasse between Lake Superior and the lower Great Lakes. However, the project was never implemented. According to Almy's plan the canal would have intersected, and thus destroyed, the army's millrace at Fort Brady. The race, under the protection of the fort's commanding officer, provided power for the post's small sawmill. Acting under instructions from his superiors in Washington, the officer and his men evicted the canal workers from the premises on 13 May 1839. Nothing further was done, and recriminations between Washington and Michigan lasted for months. It remained to be seen if Congress would respond with land or money to the petition of the Michigan legislature.[5]

Several months after the fiasco at Fort Brady, Senator John Norvell decided to launch the first major drive for federal aid to build a Sault canal. Norvell was the senior of Michigan's three members in Congress. A Democrat, he had served Michigan in the Senate since the state's admission into the Union. He considered Detroit to be his home and had been its postmaster when Michigan was still a territory.[6]

Norvell's efforts in the Twenty-fifth Congress to obtain a land grant had not reached second reading before Congress adjourned. Impressed with the need for an early start in the Twenty-sixth Congress, Norvell announced his intentions on the first day that the Senate sat for business. He would ask the Senate Committee on the Public Land to report a bill granting 100,000 acres to Michigan to finance a canal. Although his Senate colleague from Michigan, Augustus Porter, had not yet arrived to lend support, Norvell spoke from a stronger position than he had held in the previous Congress. Senator William Allen of Ohio had moved up to the Committee on Foreign Relations, and Norvell took Allen's place on the five-man Committee on the Public Land. Thus on 31 December 1839 Norvell saw his canal bill referred to his own committee. Three days later the committee reported the bill to the Senate without amendment.[7]

Clear sailing for the bill continued, as the Senate debate on the second reading revealed little opposition. Norvell defended his ideas briefly. This was to be exclusively a state work, and Michigan was not asking for one cent to aid any corporation or monopoly. Norvell would agree to an amendment to assure that the state would be the sole owner of the canal. As for the need for the canal, Norvell cited only the general commerce of the Northwest and the fishing industry of Lake Superior. He estimated the cost of the canal at $125,000 if built to accommodate sailing ships only, or $250,000 if constructed for steamships. His physical description of the canal followed the 1837 design of Almy, although he increased the cost estimate slightly.

Other senators came forward as friends of the canal project. Missouri Senator Thomas Hart Benton said that the object was not just a good one but a great one, and likened Lake Superior to the Caspian Sea. Senator John Henderson of Mississippi praised the purpose of the measure, asking only that the land granted not be sold at less than the minimum price of the rest of the public land as established by Congress. Norvell agreed to an amendment to this effect, and the Senate ordered the bill engrossed.[8]

Three days later progress came to a temporary halt. At the call for the yeas and nays for final passage, Henry Clay objected. According to Clay, the Senate was about to vote away a vast quantity of the public domain without hearing a single word in favor of the bill or the canal. This nettled Norvell, who observed that if Clay had been on the floor of the Senate during the second reading he would have heard enough. However, Norvell agreed to a postponement, and anticipated a further attack from Clay.[9]

The Senate considered the bill briefly on 14 April, and the canal forces picked up the support of Ohio's Allen and Benjamin Tappan.

John J. Crittenden of Kentucky joined Clay in opposition. The Senate approved two more amendments, but again the measure was set aside.

The major debate took place on 21 April, with Michigan's Senator Augustus Porter participating for the first time. Like Norvell, Porter lived in Detroit. He had been a member of the Senate only three months, but he was a Whig and thus a good man to answer Clay. Porter began his statement with reference to a national community-of-interest thesis. The canal would be of great value to Ohio, Illinois, Indiana, Pennsylvania, and New York as well as to Michigan, which would share with the others the benefits of increased trade. As to the nature of this trade, Porter cited the great potential in the whitefish industry. He also mentioned the fur industry and made some reference to mineral deposits that had been reported by tourists.

Porter then turned to the engineering study made by Almy, with whom he claimed a personal friendship. Although he asserted that no serious difficulties would be encountered in building the canal since the rocks would not require blasting, Porter at the same time unwittingly sent up a warning signal that any geologist would have read at once. Near the canal, he noted, were large masses of granite, so the cost of hauling backing stone for the masonry locks would be minimal. A geologist, hearing this, would have considered the possibility—or probability—of granite *under* the canal route that would indeed require blasting. Almy's map indicated only sedimentary red sandstone, but the warning existed nevertheless for those alert enough to see the danger.[10]

Clay then moved to the attack. A canal at the Sault, he declared, would be about as useful as a canal on the moon. He denounced the project as premature and asked why grants should be given to Michigan, with a population of only two or three hundred thousand, just because similar grants had been made to Ohio, with a population of two million. Clay not only rejected for the time being the national community-of-interest argument but also erred on his population figures; Ohio did not have a population of two million when it received land grants in 1827–28. South Carolina's William C. Preston joined Clay in opposition, challenging the data, surveys, and estimates. He called the Upper Peninsula "terra incognita" and feared the revival of a vast program of internal improvements.

Preston weakened his case when he denounced the bill for its failure to follow the usual system of railroad and canal land grants. Although the bill did not provide that alternate sections of land be granted along the canal route, such a proposal would have been ridiculous for a canal one mile in length. Crittenden, in his criticism of the bill, proved to be much more farsighted; he was sure that within a few years another 100,000 acres would be needed to complete the project.[11]

Norvell, in summarizing his defense of the proposal, first reiterated the national community-of-interest argument. The federal government would have free use of the canal, and a fleet could be placed on Lake Superior in the event of war with Great Britain. Moreover, the undertaking would develop and cultivate the resources of a vast region, much as the Erie Canal had brought prosperity to areas far from its actual route. The proposed canal would make available an enormous supply of ship's timber, for example, to replace the New England supply when this should be exhausted.

Norvell then proceeded to refute Preston's arguments. He suggested that the states' rights defenders should be more consistent, pointing out that the project had been conceived, designed, and finally launched in May 1839 by Michigan alone, without federal help. There was to be no partnership between Michigan and the United States. Finally, Norvell derided the alternate section plan for its obvious lack of practicality.[12]

To the backers of the canal it seemed likely that the bill would pass the Senate. Since the measure had been amended twice after engrossment, a clean copy would be needed. Tappan of Ohio, a supporter of the bill, moved to recommit to the Committee on the Public Land. Nine days later the committee reported the bill out in its clean form, and the Senate passed it without further debate. It was a pathfinding victory for Norvell.[13]

Unfortunately for the canal supporters, the bill progressed no further. House management should have been in the hands of Michigan's Isaac Crary. He had served as a Democratic congressman since Michigan's admission to the Union and, as a member of the House Committee on the Public Land, held the same position of strength in the House that Norvell did in the Senate. However, Crary was not nearly as effective as Norvell. With his home in inland Marshall, he lacked the "Great Lakes outlook" of the two senators from Detroit. In his one speech in support of the canal, he gave lip service to harbor improvement but seemed to be more interested in road development in the interior. Even here he was ineffective, for he foolishly digressed with an irrelevant attack on William Harrison's conduct of the Battle of Tippecanoe. Naturally this evoked a Whiggish outcry in the House, and Crary was almost forced to surrender the floor. His point, if he had one, was lost. Canal prospects suffered from his ineptitude, and the House Committee on the Public Land failed to report the canal bill to the full House.[14]

Despite Crary's failure, congressional canal backers gained some ground. They learned that they could win support from the other Great Lakes states, as well as from the lower Mississippi area, through the community-of-interest approach. They need only wait for a more propitious time. They did not realize that they would have to wait twelve years.

Meanwhile, despite the local setback at the Sault and the condition of the economy in general, Michigan renewed its petitions for federal aid. In 1840, as the state legislature contemplated the abandonment of state-supported internal improvement projects, a select committee of the House of Representatives continued to advocate the building of the canal, citing the immense forests of pine timber, the profitable fishing industry, the creation of a Superior District market for farm crops, the rich fur trade, and the desirability of counterbalancing British influence with the Indians through an increased American population on Lake Superior. Finally, the committee noted the presence of copper ore—but again displayed a lack of knowledge of Superior District geology in its conviction that the copper was "situated at the bottom of a most safe, commodious, and beautiful harbor." The legislature then passed a memorial to Congress asking for land, money, or both to build the canal. Copies were sent to the legislatures of New York, Pennsylvania, Ohio, Indiana, and Illinois.[15]

Michigan repeated such petitions at various intervals. The memorial signed by Governor John S. Barry in 1843 stressed the community-of-interest thesis: "The construction of the canal around the falls of the St. Mary's River, is deemed to be of the utmost importance, not only to this state but to all lake states."

Again the petition was sent not only to Washington but also to the several Great Lakes state legislatures and to the legislature of the Territory of "Wiskonsan" as well. Much the same message was repeated in 1844 and 1848.[16]

Developments in the Superior District in the 1840s did much to sustain the Michigan petitions and to reverse Clay's contention that the area might just as well be located on the moon. For about six years a copper fever raged in the land, and though it was by no means as virulent as the California gold fever that followed, it did much to attract attention and people to the area. Most of the early mining ventures were disastrous failures, but just enough succeeded to offer hope for others. For example, the successful Pittsburgh and Boston Mining Company paid its first dividend of $60,000 in 1849, and a few others were not far behind. It is difficult to estimate the number of miners and speculators who went to the Superior District between 1841 and 1847, but by 1845 fourteen companies were actively engaged in mining near Copper Harbor, and others were being organized. By 1844 the War Department established Fort Wilkins at Copper Harbor, manned by two companies of the Fifth United States Infantry.[17]

In the roadless district the little mining communities had to depend upon lake shipping to obtain supplies and to haul copper to Sault Ste. Marie. With the utmost difficulty workers hauled two brigs, the *Astor* and the *Algonquin*, around the impasse at the Sault and set them afloat on Lake Superior. On 19 September 1844 a storm destroyed the *Astor*. The War Department immediately chartered the *Algonquin* to sustain the men at Fort Wilkins, leaving the mining community to fend for itself. Shipping owners relieved the shortage in 1845, as the brigs *Ocean* and *Merchant* were hauled on rollers around the Sault. In the same year shipper Sheldon McKnight built the large schooner *Napoleon* on Lake Superior. The latter, accused of rolling enough to pick up fish in her smoke stack, would receive a steam engine in 1848. Finally, in an effort that took seven weeks, the steamer *Independence*, with a 365-ton capacity, was portaged around the rapids. By the end of 1845 the total tonnage on Lake Superior reached 635. As a result there were new demands on Congress for a canal.[18]

In 1846 the Superior District gained a new canal champion and its first newspaper when John N. Ingersoll moved from St. Clair,

Michigan, to Copper Harbor. Ingersoll was born in Westchester, New York, in 1817, the youngest of four brothers. He was orphaned at the age of eleven when his father, a New York merchant, drowned. Two years later the boy moved to New York City to learn the printing trade from Horace Greeley. The two men became lifelong friends, and in 1837 Ingersoll took the famous advice of the older man and moved to Detroit. Here he worked as a compositor for the *Free Press* and as a foreman for the *Detroit Advertiser* until 1839, when he struck out on his own and for the next seven years published newspapers in the Lower Peninsula. In 1846 he moved to Copper Harbor to publish the *Lake Superior News and Miners' Journal.* In order to help pay his way (he did not intend to publish in the winter months), he obtained a job as enrolling and engrossing clerk for the state legislature, and in 1848 he became secretary of the Michigan Senate.[19]

Once Ingersoll had set up his newspaper in this outpost of civilization, his eastern friends, including Greeley, could and did reprint his articles, and information of reasonably accurate nature began to circulate in the East. True, the *New York Express* jeered, "This is the first instance in which a newspaper precedes population." Ingersoll replied, "The motive that prompted the above item is on the par with its ignorance. We despise the one while we pity the other." For all its jeering, the *Express* had brought knowledge both of the area and of Ingersoll's editorial effort to an eastern audience. For his part Ingersoll pledged to protect the interests of the district and to foster its development.[20]

Greeley noted that Ingersoll was a man "whom it is necessary to know to form a proper estimate of mankind," and predicted that Ingersoll's paper would be distinguished for its literary and technical excellence. It was not long, however, before Ingersoll decided that he was indeed located too far in advance of civilization. The army abandoned Fort Wilkins on 24 July 1846, and in the spring of 1847 Ingersoll moved his press to Sault Ste. Marie and changed the name of his publication to *Lake Superior News and Mining Journal.*[21]

At the Sault, Ingersoll found a growing community. The original landowners had been French, and the land holdings reflected the ribbon pattern of French agricultural settlements in the New World. Narrow lots extended several miles into the countryside at right angles to the St. Mary's River. A fort had been built at the foot of the

rapids in 1822. It was named Fort Brady in 1825 and was occupied by a small garrison until 1857. A mile and a half to the southeast of the fort lay a Methodist missionary reserve of 640 acres. A Chippewa Indian reservation overlooked the rapids, and most of the villagers lived between the Indian reservation and the fort. A traveler in the area in 1846 counted about forty or fifty houses in which lived a majority of the area's 200 people. The United States operated a customshouse, a post office, and a mineral agency, the latter under the supervision of McKnight. Two hotels had been constructed in 1845, the Van Anden House by Joshua Van Anden and the St. Mary's Hotel by Moses Stevens. Within one year so many travelers arrived in the area that these two establishments were often forced to turn away guests.[22]

Many visitors to the Sault were men of letters or politics. In 1847 Greeley arrived to visit a copper mine in which he held a small interest. On 3 July he delivered a temperance lecture at the Van Anden House, but the letters that he wrote for publication were of more value to the area. "The Saut seems to me to be the most growing place I have yet seen," he wrote. He declared the Polk administration's internal improvement policy insane and called for the immediate construction of a Sault canal. His fellow Whig editor Thurlow Weed of Albany followed a few weeks later with a party that included politicians Edward Bates, Thomas King Butler, Robert C. Schenck, and Governor William Bebb of Ohio. In an editorial Weed called the government's failure to build a canal "terribly neglectful." Only Whig diarist Philip Hone, who arrived in the company of former congressman George Washington Lay, was not impressed. After almost missing his boat as a result of misplacing his diary and $500, he wrote of the Sault, "*Le jeu ne vaut pas la chandelle.*" On the other hand, author Charles Lanman had just written in his book that the construction of the proposed ship canal should not be delayed a single year.[23]

Of all the visitors Greeley offered the most sobering description of the Superior District. He noted that copper was abundant but warned against the get-rich-quick speculators, who were also abundant. Some of the mines would pay off, but only in the distant future. Greeley estimated that ten days of labor must be rendered in nonmining activity for every day actually spent in mining. All provisions and equipment must be ferried ashore in small boats, and animals would be required to swim. Workers would have to cut roads inland and build cabins before the early winter. Winter supplies must be brought up from Detroit in large quantities and at great expense. Hay cost only six dollars per ton in Detroit; after being hauled overland at the Sault, it cost between thirty and forty dollars at Copper Harbor. Greeley did not actually reverse his advice to American youth, but he warned that young men coming to the Superior District had better bring money. A canal was vital, but it was not the only improvement badly needed for the development of the district.[24]

The parade of distinguished callers continued in 1848 and in subsequent years. Alexander Wheelock Thayer, the Harvard librarian who would later write the nineteenth-century biography of Ludwig von Beethoven, paid a visit. Greeley made his second trip to the Sault. The great Harvard naturalist Louis Agassiz spent a summer on Lake Superior, unaware that his son would win a fortune in the same area. The Agassiz party included William Keller of the Lawrence Scientific School, Jules Marcou, superintendent of the Mineralogical Cabinet in Paris, J. Elliot Cabot, editor of the *Massachusetts Quarterly Review*, Dr. John LeConte, destined to become president of the University of California, and several members of the senior class at Harvard. On the evening of 17 June 1848, Agassiz lectured at the St. Mary's Hotel and, as could be expected, declared the Lake Superior whitefish to be a new species, exhibiting a minute variation from previously known whitefish. Cabot, a chronicler of the party, estimated the population of the Sault to be about one thousand, of whom the barkeepers appeared to be the only ones working. He counted, within view of the hotel, seven buildings in which liquor was sold exclusively.[25]

More than mere curiosity lay behind these visits. Ingersoll extolled the vigorous atmosphere of Sault Ste. Marie and pronounced it free from "miasons, fevers, liver diseases, dyspepsia, calomel, blue devils, and duns." Not only was the area free from blue devils and duns; it was also supposed to be free from cholera. The year 1849 saw a fresh wave of this killing disease sweep through the East, and perhaps many of the visitors came to the Sault partly to escape the epidemic. At any rate, they continued to come, among them Senator Truman Smith of Connecticut, Congressman William Henry of Vermont, Governor John S. Barry of Michigan, and the editor of the *Cleveland Herald*. The need for a canal was obvious to all the visitors, and most of them were highly articulate. They were soon to have a fresh opportunity to express their views.[26]

On 3 August 1846 President James K. Polk vetoed the River and Harbor Bill and sent a stern message to Congress: "The Constitution has not, in my judgment, conferred upon the Federal Government the power to construct works of internal improvement within the states, or to appropriate money from the Treasury for that purpose."[27] With his message Polk, the most thoroughgoing Jacksonian to enter the White House after 1836, dashed the hopes of thousands of westerners and enraged a number of influential men of all sections.

The veto message continued with the familiar lecture describing the federal government as one restricted to expressly granted powers. Although Polk did admit to the Hamiltonian view that the government could implement these powers in ways unspecified in the Constitution, his interpretation of this implementation was strict indeed. Thus lighthouses could be constructed to save the lives of citizens, but harbors and rivers could not be improved at federal expense unless they were involved in foreign trade. Polk refused to recognize that rivers and harbors could be involved in interstate commerce and so qualify for federal aid. Instead he warned of the inherent dangers in the River and Harbor Bill: power would be dangerously consolidated in the federal government, hostile sectional feelings engendered, and the harmony of Congress destroyed. Somewhat inconsistently, Polk then summoned up the specter of logrolling, which implied at least a modicum of harmony in the same Congress. Finally he referred to the Mexican War, then in progress, and concluded, "It would seem to be the dictate of wisdom under such circumstances to husband our means, and not to waste them on comparatively unimportant objects."[28]

When a president thus opts for guns instead of butter, someone usually becomes critical. In this case the caustic Hone labeled Polk's attitude "contumetious," and he and thousands of others traveled to Chicago in the summer of 1847 to see what could be done. Among the thousands attending the great River and Harbor Convention was a small but enthusiastic delegation from Sault Ste. Marie led by John Ingersoll.[29]

There were other reasons besides the Polk veto for holding the

Chicago convention. With the Oregon question settled, ambitious merchants anticipated a trade network that might extend to the Orient if the federal government would help. Greeley complained that Canada's Welland Canal was diverting much of the Great Lakes trade to Montreal, and demanded that Washington do something about it. Colonel J. J. Abert, commanding the Corps of Topographical Engineers, recorded an opinion that the Great Lakes constituted a nursery for seamen who would be available to the nation in time of emergency, and that the government should share the cost of running and improving the nursery.[30]

The Polk veto meant the sacrifice of a variety of plans in many different parts of the country. Buffalo's harbor badly needed improvement, a concern for anyone using the Erie Canal; now federal funds would not be forthcoming. The bill had provided $75,000 for work on the Hudson River. The merchants of Oswego lost a $10,000 harbor improvement project. Other harbors destined to go unimproved included those at Ashtabula, Cleveland, Sandusky, Grand River, Michigan City, Racine, Milwaukee, and Chicago. Ingersoll could well reason that if presidents should continue to block all these, his own canal project would have no chance. He wrote, "The time is past when even the west alone can be trifled with."[31]

With nineteen states officially represented, the convention settled down to serious business. Each state was permitted a vote equal to its numerical strength in Congress. The throng then listened to messages of approval from dignitaries who were not able to attend: Clay, Benton, Van Buren, and Michigan's Senator Alpheus Felch. The message from Lewis Cass, senator from Michigan, was an enigma. With his eye on the Democratic presidential nomination in 1848, Cass refused to endorse the convention; he simply regretted his inability to attend. The audience was incredulous, and the Cass letter was read a second time. Perhaps no other state had been as badly hurt by the Polk veto as Michigan, and Greeley treated the Cass message with contempt. Cass's political ambitions remained a formidable obstacle for Sault canal advocates for the next four years.[32]

The convention was determined that unanimous agreement should not be endangered by the proponents of specific projects. The delegates succeeded in tabling all motions relating to the St. Lawrence River, a Pacific railroad, and other improvements. If

Ingersoll was disappointed that there would be no action taken on his project, he did not indicate it. In a scene described as "animated and exciting in the highest degree," the delegates by unanimous vote adopted sixteen general resolutions. The first was of little help to Ingersoll. Regarding the constitutionality of internal improvements, the principle of the "common interests" of the states should be evoked when an act of improvement required the concurrence of two or more states. A canal at the Sault, of course, would require the approval of Michigan only. Ensuing resolutions were more favorable to Ingersoll. Since the federal government had preempted control over foreign and interstate commerce, the government must afford all facilities that the individual states could have afforded had the revenue and authority remained with the states. The convention demanded that the same treatment be given to inland water routes as to Atlantic ports. It roundly denounced Polk for his lack of faith in democratic processes. Since the delegates were aware of the Whig domination of the convention, they proceeded to disclaim any association with a single political party. Finally, the convention agreed to establish a permanent executive committee to collect and publish facts in the hope of enforcing the will of the convention on the president and Congress.[33]

The Executive Committee of the River and Harbor Convention sent its memorial to Congress in June 1848; the lengthy document must have been a disappointment to Ingersoll. It contained no specific mention of a canal at the Sault and paid scant attention to Lake Superior problems. In fact, the committee cited the mud flats of Lake St. Clair at the foot of Lake Huron as the priority project rather than the rapids of the remote St. Mary's River. For the most part, however, the document concentrated on the constitutional question, refuting Polk's veto message without mentioning the president by name.[34]

The convention had no immediate influence on Polk, and the so-called Wisconsin Improvement Bill of 1847 had no chance with the president. His veto message of 15 December 1847 was simply a repetition of the 1846 statement. It was obvious that nothing could be accomplished until the nation elected a new president. Whig hopes hinged upon a military hero and Polk's determination to retire after one term, and the enigmatic Cass loomed larger on Democratic national horizons.[35]

In the long run the River and Harbor Convention was more

influential, for it stimulated the awareness of a national community-of-interest. Editors would keep alive the inspiration of the convention in the months to come. Greeley would cite Ingersoll in his columns, Weed would cite Greeley, and the Cleveland *Daily Herald* would cite Ingersoll and others. All would preserve the spirit of Chicago until the time for actual accomplishment should arrive.[36]

2 Failure of State Financing And an Act of Congress

Michigan's problems with the canal project were not unique; by 1850 the general experience in financing public improvements in the Old Northwest ranged from unsettling to disastrous. An internal improvement project could be financed by the state alone, as was the case with the early Michigan railroads, or it could be financed on a "mixed" basis. Ohio, for example, experimented in mixed enterprise beginning with the passage of the Ohio Loan Law of 1837. The law was based on the principle that the state should stand as a financing partner with private investors to build railroads, canals, and turnpikes. The Ohio law was not original; older states had tried it first. Its greatest defect was the failure of the legislature to place a maximum limit on the amount the state could commit. When construction costs far exceeded estimates, Ohio faced bankruptcy; and yet the transportation system in the state was excellent. Table 1 indicates the share of public investment in canal construction in the United States.[1]

Between 1839 and 1850 Michigan went through the same boom-bust-recovery cycle that affected Ohio and the other states of the Old Northwest. In the case of Michigan, banking practice and population growth were largely responsible for the familiar pattern. A general banking law passed in 1837 made it possible for anyone meeting certain conditions to go into banking without a special act of the state legislature. It was the first such law in the United States, and it coincided with a population boom in Michigan. In the early days the state's population growth was slow. The land in southeast Michigan was poor, and potential settlers usually pushed west to better lands in Ohio and Indiana. The completion of the Erie Canal in 1825 made the farmlands of the Old Northwest more attractive, and by 1847 canal trade from western states exceeded that originating in New York. The situation was reflected in population changes. The federal census of 1840 indicated that in one decade Michigan's population had increased sevenfold, to 212,267. The combination of easy credit through questionable banking practice and population influx led to wild land speculation that could have only one result.[2]

TABLE 1

PUBLIC INVESTMENT IN CANALS, 1815-1860

(in millions of dollars)

Year	Public Investment	Total Investment	Public Investment as a Percentage of Total
1815-34	41.2	58.6	70.3
1834-44	57.3	72.2	79.4
1844-60	38.0	57.4	66.3
TOTAL	136.5	188.2	73.4

SOURCE: Harvey H. Segal, "Cycles of Canal Construction," in *Canals and American Economic Development*, by Carter Goodrich et al. (New York, 1961), p. 215.

Until the bust came the enthusiasm was infectious. The same legislature that passed the general banking law launched the state on a most ambitious program of internal improvements. Unfortunately, Michigan followed the example of other Old Northwest states as well as the states of the East by committing too much state money to the projects. Indeed, Michigan's original state constitution made state-financed internal improvements an imperative, and the Michigan legislature authorized construction of three canals and three railroads to be financed by the state alone.[3]

Population density and sectional rivalry dictated the location of the three railroads, all with an east-west orientation. The state would construct the Michigan Southern through the southern tier of counties, the Michigan Central through the next tier north, and the Michigan Northern through the fourth tier. Of the canals one would be long, crossing most of the state from east to west and linking the waters of Lake St. Clair (and thus Lake Erie) to the Kalamazoo

River (and thus Lake Michigan). The other two would be short; one would link the Saginaw and Maple rivers, completing the second east-west waterway through the Lower Peninsula, and the other would bypass the rapids of the St. Mary's River.[4]

The same spirit of sectionalism that dictated the location of Michigan's railroads dictated the sale of the railroads to private ownership in 1846. Political rivalry played no part in this decision. After the banking panic of 1837 and the general depression that followed, Michigan found it impossible to finance all her internal improvements, some at various stages of completion. A bill to rescue any one of them would have been doomed to sectional defeat in the legislature. In addition, the Michigan Central needed a fresh infusion of capital to replace track already worn. Furthermore, Michigan experienced the same wave of hostility toward state-built internal improvements that was sweeping through the other Old Northwest states, although it took several years to formalize this new spirit in state constitutions. The reason was simple, and it did not matter if the state followed the "mixed" financing system of Ohio or the direct system of Michigan. With a few exceptions like the profitable Michigan Central, the improvements lost money, and tax increases seemed imminent. Under such circumstances the doctrine of laissez faire was easily asserted and fell upon receptive ears.[5]

The new Michigan constitution of 1850, reversing the policy set forth in its predecessor, prohibited state participation in internal improvements: "The state shall not subscribe to, or be interested in, the stock of any company, association, or corporation." However, the constitutional convention did leave a loophole in the event that Congress should be generous in the future: "The state shall not be a party to . . . any work of internal improvement . . . except in expenditure of grants to the state of land or other property." Thus did Michigan in severe financial straits assume a subsidiary role in financing internal improvements. The state would now become little more than the disbursing and supervising agent of the federal government.[6]

During the depression Michigan was forced either to risk repudiation of state bonds or to sell, and the state elected the latter course. A private company purchased the Michigan Central for $2,000,000; another, the Michigan Southern for $500,000. Construction of the Michigan Northern had not begun, and only minute fractions of the two Lower Peninsula canals were completed. The proposed canal at the Sault ended in the Smith and Driggs fiasco of 1839. Even with the sale it took Michigan over half a century to redeem its bonds.[7]

In spite of economic setbacks, Michigan's population continued to grow. The census of 1850 indicated a white population of 395,071, with almost 80 percent located in the three southern tiers of counties. The census also revealed a population of 890 in Chippewa County and 707 in Houghton County, the only counties in the Upper Peninsula. In the past when Sault Canal advocates had presented their arguments, their emphasis had usually been placed on lumber and whitefish, with mineral resources noted almost as an afterthought. That day was over, and the presence of over 700 people in Houghton County could mean only one thing—mining. Official reports confirmed this activity. In 1850 the Michigan legislature published the report of Stephen V. R. Trowbridge, assistant agent of United States Mineral Lands. Trowbridge wrote that there were seven copper mines active in the Upper Peninsula, that five of these had already made shipments, and that one, the Pittsburgh and Boston Cliff Mine, had already paid a dividend. This last company employed more than 200 men. Congress had also ordered copies printed of several other geological surveys, all indicating the presence of vast deposits of copper. Canal supporters were bound to switch their emphasis to copper, and Sault editor John Ingersoll was in the position to take the lead.[8]

In the fall of 1848, Ingersoll launched his major press campaign for a Sault Canal. Democrats of the Sault had elected him president of their caucus, and Ingersoll took the opportunity to lash out at Polk. He called the government cruelly oppressive in its failure to grant aid for a canal and said that Michigan's maritime coast had been almost completely neglected in favor of improvements in the East. The caucus applauded Ingersoll's words and pledged support for the presidential aspirations of Lewis Cass. Ingersoll was also forced to deal with competition from within the state to secure federal aid. The House of Representatives had tabled at third reading a bill granting 500,000 acres to Michigan to build a canal between Lake St. Clair and Lake Michigan, an attempt to revive the Clinton and Kalamazoo project of 1837. Obviously Congress could not be expected to make two grants to Michigan at the same time. Ingersoll denounced the proposed canal as being strictly a local project, whereas the Sault canal would be of national importance. Besides, southern Michigan, with two railroads, already had a transportation system.[9]

Ingersoll was not alone in his efforts. In 1849 the Michigan legislature tried a slightly different approach. In an obvious effort to attract the attention of the Empire State, it petitioned Congress to finance a canal around Niagara Falls and then amended the petition to include the Sault canal as well. Trowbridge testified to Congress that the impasse at the Sault constituted a serious block to the development of the Superior District. United States geologists J. W. Foster and J. D. Whitney made a similar report and urged the construction of a canal. A meeting of Sault citizens voted to send three men, led by Judge Samuel Ashmun, to plead their cause in Washington.[10]

Eventually Ingersoll reached the end of his financial—if not emotional—strength. He recorded his solitary celebration of the Fourth of July, 1848, complete with a long series of toasts—all made by himself to himself. He ended the publishing year with an admission of severe financial difficulties. When, at the conclusion of the next publishing year, the situation had not improved, he requested payment from his debtors while asking patience from his creditors. Apparently this effort was of no avail, and in 1849 Ingersoll abandoned publishing efforts at the Sault. Meanwhile, in October of 1848 a caucus of Sault Democrats had nominated him as their candidate for the Michigan House of Representatives on a canal platform, and in November he had defeated his Whig opponent by a narrow margin. Once he was in Lansing, his colleagues recognized his abilities by electing him Speaker. He remained a Democrat until 1858 when he switched to the Republican party.[11]

The Sault was not to be deprived of a newspaper, and a new man came forward to take Ingersoll's place. In the spring of 1850, J. Venen Brown began to publish the *Lake Superior Journal*. It was a completely new venture in all ways, including a new font and advertising that was oriented more toward Detroit and Cleveland than toward the Sault. Brown lost little time in pledging his support for the canal project. Unfortunately he was not as skilled a writer as was his predecessor; his first sentence in support of the canal ran thirty-six lines in print. On the other hand, there was nothing wrong with his power of political observation. He regretted that the political clash over slavery threatened to divert minds from "more legitimate channels of legislation."[12]

Brown did not have long to wait before the building of a canal became a matter of human necessity and not merely an economic convenience. At the opening of the 1851 navigating season, there were four steamships on Lake Superior plus a small fleet of schooners. The propellers and their capacities were the *Manhattan* (3,000 barrels), the *Monticello* (2,500 barrels), the *Independence* (2,000 barrels), and the old *Napoleon* (800 barrels), still catching fish in her smoke stack. The aggregate capacity of the schooners was estimated at 1,000 barrels. To haul a ship over the portage cost between $1,000 and $3,000, depending upon size, and the effort was enormous. Thus Lake Superior economics dictated that only a fleet of minimum capacity be brought across the portage. Any excess capacity would go to waste inasmuch as it would be too inconvenient and costly to bring a ship back down.[13]

Disaster struck in 1851. The *Independence* had been driven ashore in the previous winter and was not made seaworthy until July. Delivery of supplies thus fell behind schedule at the outset. Then, on 1 August, the *Monticello* and the *Manhattan* collided. The *Manhattan* was saved only by her cargo of lumber, but she was out of service for the rest of the year. On 25 September the damaged *Monticello* foundered with a cargo of twenty-five tons of copper ore, and her 100 passengers and crew reached shore only after undergoing great hardship. Thus, three months before the close of navigation, the Superior District lost over half its cargo-carrying capacity, which had been miniscule to begin with.[14]

Stores began to pile up immediately at the Sault. Shipowner Sheldon McKnight ordered the *Baltimore* north from Detroit to replace his lost *Monticello*, but she could not be portaged around the falls until winter. The remaining ships on Lake Superior had to carry the burden, and their captains took risks to meet the demand. The *Napoleon* made the last trip into Marquette, where the population had been without flour for six weeks. Brown estimated that 18,000 barrels of provisions and supplies were stranded at the Sault at the close of the navigation season. He pointed out that if

three steamers had been lost instead of two, the result would have
been famine, and cried for government aid in the name of
humanity.[15]

Brown's political fears were now realized. The Thirty-first
Congress was too preoccupied with problems created by the victory
over Mexico to worry about a Sault canal. In his inaugural address
President Zachary Taylor stated that, although he was willing to
recommend such constitutional measures in support of internal
improvements as he thought fitting and necessary, the Congress
itself must regulate domestic policy. What he would have done with
a Sault canal bill must remain a matter for conjecture. Even as
ardent a canal proponent as Brown would have had to admit that
the problems of California, with a population of over 100,000 and
no territorial government, must receive prior consideration.[16]

On 9 July 1850 Zachary Taylor died, and the way was cleared for
the passage of the Compromise of that year. The Congress had been
in session for 302 days, its longest session to date, and with the
passage the pressure eased immediately. Most of the members
thought that the knotty problems related to slavery had been solved
for all time. The new Whig president, Millard Fillmore, had realized
an ambition born at the Chicago River and Harbor Convention,
where he had endorsed the concept of federal support for internal
improvements benefiting the national community. If the next
Congress retained the same amiable mood, perhaps the canal bill
could be passed before the outbreak of new storms. The president
would be no problem.[17]

In December 1851 the Thirty-second Congress met for the first
time, with the Democrats in control of both houses. Early in the
following year, leaders in Detroit prepared to apply pressure for a
Sault canal. Mayor Zach Chandler called a meeting at City Hall that
included McKnight, Ingersoll, Brown, Whig politician Jacob
Howard, and James Joy, head of the firm of Joy and Porter and
legal counsel for the Michigan Central Railroad. The men drew up a
petition to Congress and called for a mass meeting in Detroit for the
night of 9 January. The meeting was a success, and many signed the
petition, which stressed the national need for copper; Superior
District iron ore, thought to be the best in the world, was considered
second in importance.[18]

News of the mass meeting spread throughout the Midwest. The

Plain Dealer of Cleveland came to the support of the project and urged the Ohio legislature to add its petition. In February the Indiana legislature entered its plea, with the New York senate joining in the same month. In March, United States Senator Richard Broadhead of Pennsylvania presented the petition of the legislature of his state. Meanwhile, a delegation from Michigan traveled to Washington to add its influence. The group included shipowners McKnight and E. B. Ward, prominent citizens John Burt and Peter White, State Representative Abner Sherman, and Brown.[19]

Weeks passed, and Congress took no action. The culprit was Lewis Cass, whose influence was essential to the passage of a canal bill. Cass, the defeated Democratic presential candidate in 1848, badly wanted the nomination in 1852 and knew that he must alienate as few Democrats as possible. He had brought derision on his head by his avoidance of the Chicago River and Harbor Convention in 1847, and his conduct in the debate over the Compromise of 1850 had also been disappointing. In the end equivocation did him no good. Although he led on the first ballot at the Democratic Convention of 1852 and reached a peak of 135 votes on the thirty-fifth ballot, the Democrats nominated the New Hampshire doughface Franklin Pierce on the forty-ninth ballot. Greeley realized the significance of the sequence. *Now* the time was ripe for the passage of the canal bill. Passage would have been useless under Polk, impossible under Taylor, and inexpedient for Cass prior to the convention. Should Pierce become president, the situation would revert to the Polk impasse. In fact, although Greeley could not foresee it, after four years of Pierce in the White House the old hostilities would be so revived as to make passage under the next president all but impossible. As long as Fillmore remained president, however, canal chances were good. When Cass finally did make his first speech for the canal, the *Detroit Daily Advertiser* grumbled, "After being defeated, and disappointed, he has at last found out that he owes a duty to his own state."[20]

On 11 August, Cass called upon the chairman of the Senate Finance Committee to bring Michigan Senator Alpheus Felch's canal bill to the floor, and on 16 August the Senate considered the subject. Cass refused to defend the bill on the grounds of its obvious advantage for internal commerce; instead he resorted to the plea of military necessity. As long as Britain owned Canada, the United States must be ready for a war on the Great Lakes. With a canal armed vessels could pass to and from Lake Superior as necessity dictated. This approach drew an immediate attack from Andrew Butler of South Carolina, who sputtered that the nation had been at peace with Britain for forty years. Furthermore the British would never dare attack Michigan; one speech from Cass, and Michigan men would attack the British fleet on horseback. Undiverted by Cass's military red herring, Butler correctly identified the commercial nature of the canal venture, and Joseph Underwood of Kentucky wondered why, using the Cass logic, the snags could not be removed from the Mississippi.[21]

As debate continued, Felch offered a major amendment to his own bill. Instead of a grant of 750,000 acres to Michigan, he asked for an appropriation of $400,000 to build a canal, the entire project to be under the direction of the secretary of war. This would convert the legislation into a "money bill" instead of a "land bill," a change favored by many westerners. Cass and Felch were able to persuade only two other Democrats to agree, however, and the Senate defeated the money amendment. It then ordered the bill engrossed by a vote of twenty-eight to twenty-one.[22]

The vote crossed both party and sectional lines. Exactly seven Whigs gave Cass his margin of victory, while eleven voted "no." Ten Democrats voted against the bill, while twenty-one voted "yes." As might be expected, the measure won unanimous support from the Old Northwest, but it also found favor in the Mississippi Valley in the deep south. Support was unanimous in Louisiana and Arkansas, Texas and Alabama contributed one vote each with no dissents, and Florida gave both votes. Opposition was unanimous in the south Atlantic states (except Florida), Tennessee, and Kentucky. New England was divided.[23]

On 25 August the Senate bill was considered in the House, where it was defended by Michigan's C. E. Stuart. Debate was desultory until James Orr of South Carolina asked a pertinent question. He noted that the cost of the canal was estimated at $450,000, and that the bill entailed 750,000 acres. At $1.25 an acre the land should bring in $1,000,000. Why? Stuart replied that the Senate had put in that figure to assure that in any contingency there would be sufficient funds to complete the canal. The land would not be wasted, since

any not used for the canal would revert to the United States. Stuart
thus fooled the House and perhaps himself, for the bill was worded
to have the opposite result. Since there was no incentive to
economize on land, Michigan might as well grant all of it for a
canal.[24]

The bill passed the House with ease, 115 to 48. Again the vote
crossed party lines with a majority of both parties in favor. The
sectional pattern was similar to that in the Senate. Not a single vote
was cast against the bill by a congressman from the Mississippi
Valley. The five negative votes from Tennessee and Kentucky were
cast by eastern district men. The Atlantic south was all but
unanimous in opposition, but New England was more favorable,
voting "yes" fifteen to four. With the exception of Ohio, the states of
the Old Northwest were not sufficiently populated to carry much
weight in the House. The burden of passage fell upon Ohio,
Pennsylvania, and New York, the states that would gain the most
from the canal. They responded with sixty-three favorable votes and
only three negative. The community-of-interest thesis had worked
at last, and Fillmore signed the bill.[25]

It was not difficult to account for the support from the lower
Mississippi. The theory of the all-pervasiveness of sectionalism in
the decade 1841–52 is an oversimplification.[26] The Mississippi men
might have anticipated the return of the favor at some future date.
Also, there was the matter of the Fox-Wisconsin project. In 1846
Congress had granted to the Territory of Wisconsin 260,000 acres to
build a canal through the portage between the Fox and Wisconsin
rivers and in general to improve and maintain a water passage
between Lake Michigan and the Mississippi. A southerner might
have envisioned New Orleans as a port for the wealth of the Superior
District once the project was completed. In 1852 he had no way of
knowing that the perversity of the Wisconsin River would render
this only a dream.

In its final form the law carried the formidable title "An Act
Granting to the State of Michigan the Right of Way, and a
Donation of Public Land for the Construction of a Ship Canal
around the Falls of St. Mary's River in said State." Fortunately,
only public lands were involved at the canal site, or the law's passage
might have been delayed. In 1820 Secretary of War Calhoun had
instructed Lewis Cass to procure the extinction of the Indian title to

an area at the Sault not to exceed ten square miles. This was accomplished, and the Chippewa Indians received a reservation. Now, in 1852, the Indians would have to move, since the canal would pass through the reservation as well as through government lands at Fort Brady. Michigan also received a strip of land 400 feet wide along the line of the canal. The act warned that the canal must follow the line of the survey already made for that purpose by Captain Augustus Canfield, of the Corps of Topographical Engineers, in 1839. Any deviation from this line must have the express approval of the secretary of war.[27]

Canal depth as stated in the law must be 12 feet; the minimum width must be 100 feet. The act gave Michigan some leeway in determining the dimensions of the locks. Each lock was to be at least 250 feet long and at least 50 feet wide. By implication Michigan could bargain for larger locks if it seemed advisable or opportune to do so. As was right and proper, Congress made no further attempt to describe the physical characteristics of the canal. Nothing was written regarding such matters as basins, docks, and channel dredging. Michigan would have to look after the details.

The land to be granted, totaling 750,000 acres in Michigan, must be selected by an agent or agents of the governor. The secretary of the interior must approve all such selections, which were to be submitted in standard survey form. Rights of prior entry must be respected by all concerned. The land granted to Michigan could be used for no purpose other than the building of the canal. Before the state of Michigan could dispose of any of the land, the route of the canal must be established and plats filed with the secretary of war and the commissioner of the General Land Office. In other words, Michigan could legally distribute the land before the canal was actually completed.

Congress decreed that the work on the canal must be under way within three years and completed within ten. If at the end of ten years the canal had not been completed, Michigan would be forced to pay the United States a minimum of $1.50 an acre for all the grant land sold to date, and the rest would be returned to the public domain. The title of all purchases would remain valid. The Michigan legislature must order that an accurate accounting be made of the sales and net proceeds of the land.

Congress made the standard stipulation in transportation grants.

All United States vessels must be permitted to use the canal free of toll or other charge. Ships using the canal to transport troops must also pass free. The Michigan legislature must report each year to the secretary of the interior on the operation of the canal. The state could charge only such tolls as would be needed for repairs and maintenance. This last was not a standard provision, and the canal would not produce the revenue of earlier land grant canals.[28]

When Fillmore signed the bill, the responsibilities of the federal government ended as long as Michigan obeyed the law, and the state became the supervising and disbursing agent. It remained to be seen if Michigan would be as generous to potential canal builders as Congress had been.

3 Rushed Plans and Hurried Estimates

The 1852 law's provision for a land grant rather than a money grant evoked great bitterness in several places. The Cleveland *Daily Herald* considered the defeat of the Felch amendment as bad as a defeat for the bill itself, and the *Detroit Daily Advertiser* tried to make political capital over the issue by citing the votes of the Pierce men who voted against the amendment. J. Venen Brown was beside himself with rage. In an editorial headed "Saut Canal Bill Overboard," he predicted that the House would never pass the bill without the Felch amendment. Though proved wrong, he still insisted that it would take years before the Michigan authorities could find a way to convert the land into a canal. He excoriated Cass and Felch for putting up a sham fight for the Sault and demanded to know how Cass could have expected to lead the nation when on the amendment he and Felch could command the vote of only two other Democratic senators.[1]

In one week, however, Brown went through an extraordinary reversal of opinion. He had bemoaned the fate of the canal on 8 September, but on 15 September he was exuberant at the prospect. This time his editorial was headed "Saut Canal—Good Chance for Capitalists." Brown suggested that the legislature authorize the governor to receive bids based on the plans and specifications prepared by a governor-appointed engineer. The contract could then be let out to the bidder with the best surety who would agree to build the canal for the smallest grant of land. Brown proposed that the land be selected by the contracting party (absolutely legal under the law just passed by Congress, which merely required that the governor approve of the land agents) and awarded in four installments as the work progressed. Above all, he emphasized the ease with which the canal could be built, stating that two-thirds of the excavation would be in loose sandstone and the remainder in sand and gravel. Limestone of high quality could be obtained from islands in the St. Mary's River and easily transported to the site. He estimated that the total cost of the project would be $300,000.[2]

There was a good reason for Brown's dramatic change of heart. On the same page of the *Lake Superior Journal* carrying his enthusiastic message, he published a statement of high praise for the firm of E. & T. Fairbanks and its product, the Fairbanks scale. Brown also noted the arrival at the Sault of a Fairbanks agent, young (twenty-three) Charles Thompson Harvey. The two men had met while Harvey was in the area to establish sales agencies for Fairbanks, and it was Harvey who realized the potential of the canal project for his employer. He obviously sold the idea to Brown, whose editorial reversal was clearly more than a coincidence, and he set out to do he same with Erastus Fairbanks.[3]

There were three talented brothers in the firm of E. & T. Fairbanks. Erastus, the eldest, was president and general man of business for the firm. Thaddeus, next born, was a man of considerable inventive genius. His most famous invention, and the foundation of the Fairbanks fortune, was the platform scale. The youngest brother, Joseph, was a man of letters who had been educated to the bar. By the 1850s the firm was so successful that its president looked for new financial and political challenges. He probably instructed agents like Harvey to stay alert for profitable new enterprises; meanwhile, in 1852 he himself became governor of Vermont.[4]

Upon being notified by Harvey of the possibility of canal construction at the Sault, Fairbanks realized that the project would be too great for one man to finance. Accordingly, he set out in early November 1852 to call on Erastus Corning, a friend living in Albany, New York. Among his many enterprises, Corning was president of the Utica and Schenectady Railroad and held a financial interest in the Michigan Central. The connection between railroads and scales was obvious, and any project that would link Fairbanks and Corning would advance the interests of E. & T. Fairbanks Company. Fairbanks had, in fact, previously asked Corning to use his influence with the superintendent of the

Michigan Central to encourage the railroad's adoption of he Fairbanks scales.[5]

For his part Corning was one of the most powerful financiers in New York. Although he considered himself to be primarily a merchant, his interests were extensive. He owned the Albany Iron Works, had a thriving iron import business, was president of the Albany City Bank, and owned stock in six other New York banks.

Fig. 2.   Erastus Corning I, by Charles Loring Elliott (1812-1868). Collection Albany Institute of History and Art. Reproduced by permission.

Fig. 3.   Charles G. Harvey, 1884. Reproduced from the collections of the Michigan Department of State, State Archives.

Corning's interests extended to the West as well. In the 1830s he obtained a financial interest in the Farmers and Mechanics Bank in Detroit, and by 1850 he owned part of the Michigan Insurance Company, also in Detroit. He speculated in land both in New York and in the West. At the same time Corning by 1852 had acquired a prominent position in the Democratic party. A western friend had suggested that if Lewis Cass could not obtain the 1852 presidential nomination Corning might be offered to the convention as being more acceptable to the West than his friend William Marcy. Others suggested that Corning might be an excellent candidate for governor of New York. It was a remarkable record for a man who had been crippled for life in a childhood accident.[6]

Fairbanks's trip to Albany proved to be in vain, for Corning was out of the city. The Vermont man had to be satisfied with writing a lengthy letter outlining the entire proposal as envisioned by Harvey. Fairbanks told Corning he thought the canal could be constructed for no more than $275,000, but in order to be sure he ordered Harvey to prepare to return to the Sault with an engineer for a more thorough examination. The compensation for building the canal would be 750,000 acres in Michigan. Fairbanks realized that the award might seem too great in the eyes of the public; he therefore proposed to Corning that a company be formed with an authorized capitalization of $600,000. "This sum," he wrote, "might be held out as the nominal or probable expense of the work, and the lands would not be regarded an extravagant compensation for so heavy an outlay." What Fairbanks conceived as a policy of overcapitalization to fool the public proved to be the salvation of the organization that built the canal. Before long he would need every dollar of the capital issue.[7]

Fairbanks assured Corning that Harvey had found western men willing to carry about one-third of the financial burden. For the remaining $400,000, Fairbanks proposed that he and Corning each assume responsibility for $100,000, that John Seymour of Utica furnish another equal amount, and that the balance be furnished by a party mutually agreed upon. As for Harvey, Fairbanks praised him for his energy, shrewdness, and business capacity, although he had known the younger man for fewer than fifteen months. He stated that liberal provisions must be made for Harvey in the event that the project proved feasible, since Harvey was responsible for the inception of the idea and would be invaluable in its execution.[8]

For Harvey the month of October was a time of anticipation and preparation. He notified J. Venen Brown that he wanted to retain the editor for advice and help on the canal project (a request he would later have ample reason to regret); and when the order came from Fairbanks to proceed, he was ready. He returned to the Sault in November with engineer L. L. Nichols to obtain a cost estimate.[9]

Nichols had some canal experience, but he had no idea of the difficulties inherent in a construction project in the remote and rugged Upper Peninsula. For three years he had served as resident engineer, eastern subdivision, middle division, of the Erie Canal. In this capacity he had superintended minor enlargement projects, but little more. Long before he had finished with the Sault Canal he would be a much wiser man.[10]

In December, Nichols submitted his cost estimate. Allowing for the most favorable contingencies, the engineer estimated that the maximum cost would be $403,500. At this stage Nichols admitted that he was doing a certain amount of guessing. He thought that the excavation would be 30 percent rock, but he could not be sure. He did note that there were numerous granite boulders to remove. He assumed, on the basis of the most casual inspection, that limestone for the lock walls could be obtained from Lime Island, forty miles below the Sault in the St. Mary's River. His greatest error lay in the assumption that the working season at the Sault lasted nine months a year, a misconception that led to his underestimating the number of men needed for the work. A work season of seven months, May through November, would have been more accurate. Nichols did, however, warn the eastern men that he could not be sure of a number of his calculations. If Fairbanks and Corning were not alert to the possibility of error, it was their own fault.[11]

It would have been easy for any group of canal promoters to be lulled into a false sense of security regarding the ultimate cost and the time required to complete a canal at the Sault. The great canal showpiece in the United States at the time was New York's exploit of the 1820s, the Erie Canal—a profitable venture even before its formal opening in 1825. Such a success would naturally evoke imitation in other sections of the nation, and deceptive cost and construction time comparisons were inevitable.[12]

How, then, did the Erie project compare with the proposed effort at the Sault? In the first place, the Erie Canal, running from Buffalo to Albany, traversed 363 miles as compared with the 1-mile passage required in Upper Michigan. The drop in elevation between the nominal level of Lake Erie and the Hudson River was 565 feet; the comparable drop in the St. Mary's River was 19 feet at maximum. The New York engineers were forced to design and construct no fewer than eighty-three locks, whereas the Sault engineers would need but two.

The differences in the depth of the two canals required cautious comparison. The original depth of the Erie Canal was only four feet, and the Sault canal would be twelve. However, the Erie Canal had to pass through a cut in a ridge west of Lockport requiring a seven-mile excavation, of which two miles were cut through solid rock. The depth of this excavation varied from thirteen to thirty feet. Even if the entire Sault works were to be cut through solid rock (which was not the case), the maximum length of the excavation would be less than one mile. Moreover, the Erie engineers faced other problems not found at the Sault; for example, the Erie Canal had to be carried over several rivers.[13]

Two specific comparisons emerged. The total cost of the Erie Canal was $7,143,789. The total construction time had been 101 months. Would it not be reasonable for the Sault builders to assume that their canal, less than one three-hundredths of the Erie in length, would cost no more than one-eighth of that model? Would it not also be logical to assume that the Sault canal could be completed in less than one-fifth of the time required for the Erie Canal? It should be easy![14]

Corning and Fairbanks had yet another model available if they had cared to look for it. The Louisville and Portland (L. & P.) Canal on the Ohio River had been completed in 1831, and there were marked similarities between this work and the canal proposed for the Sault. Both were short, deepwater works designed to circumvent falls and rapids. In each case an earlier attempt had failed. As time went on, other parallels emerged. The builders of both canals made enemies along the way. Both canals were plagued with unrealistic cost estimates, and both far exceeded these estimates. Neither canal could have been completed without federal aid, although in the case of the L. & P. Congress first purchased stock and later purchased forfeited stock. Finally, both canals soon became obsolete. There was one major difference between the canals. Congress did not restrict the tolls of the L. & P. as it did those at the Sault, and the L. & P. made money for its stockholders and Kentucky.[15]

The directors of the soon-to-be-formed Sault company were more familiar with the Erie Canal. Two of them, Erastus Corning and his close associate John V. L. Pruyn, lived in Albany, the eastern terminal of the canal. Corning, the railroad organizer, preferred to travel by water when he could, a bias that eventually lost him the New York Central to Cornelius Vanderbuilt. He was well aware of the problems as well as the assets of water communication. Pruyn too had an interest in canals, and had assisted in a small way in obtaining funds for the enlargement of the Erie Canal in 1853. Another New Yorker, John Seymour, came from a family involved in Erie Canal projects for two generations. His brother Horatio Seymour, governor of New York in 1853–55 and 1863–65, was a strong backer of Erie Canal enlargement in 1852, the year before John, also well versed in canal problems, was elected a director of the Sault project. Their father Henry had been an acting commissioner and a longtime power in the Erie. In fact, it would have been impossible to rise in New York politics in the era 1815–60 without having played a role either for or against the Erie Canal.[16]

Two more future directors of the Sault project, John W. Brooks, of the Michigan Central Railroad, and James Joy, the road's attorney, were professionally responsible for detailed knowledge of transportation cost problems in the Midwest. Another, John Murray Forbes of Boston, though more isolated from canal theory and practice by geography, was president of the Michigan Central in 1852. Of the seven ultimate directors, only Erastus Fairbanks was a neophyte in transportation problems. The others could easily have been too optimistic in their expections regarding construction time and cost thanks to their knowledge of the Erie Canal model.[17]

Upon receiving from Washington the news of the passage of the canal bill, Michigan's Governor Robert McClelland faced a serious problem. Like Fairbanks and Corning he had no plans or specifications, but his legislature would require specific information before acting. The navigation season was nearing its close; unless McClelland could get an engineer to the Sault, the survey could not be made until the following May or June. The Michigan legislature, which met briefly every year, would meet in January 1853.

Something would have to be done at once, or a year would be wasted, and such a delay would be intolerable.[18]

McClelland knew that in the following year one of two men would enter the White House—Franklin Pierce or Winfield Scott. Scott's associates deliberately masked their candidate's attitude toward internal improvements (and almost everything else), but critics of Pierce described him as "the most undeviating foe of internal improvements that ever occupied a seat in Congress."[19] In addition, McClelland knew that unknowns would occupy the offices of secretary of war and secretary of interior. (The Michigan governor could not dream, in September 1852, that he himself would be the new secretary of the interior.) A hostile president or key cabinet member could cause serious trouble for the project.

There were other reasons for haste that McClelland could not anticipate. Should the successful bidders on the canal project wish to incorporate through an act of an eastern legislature, they too might be confronted with a time problem, since an eastern legislature might not act until the granting of a canal contract. McClelland had to face the Michigan problem first, however, and he asked Secretary of War C. M. Conrad for the services of an army engineer to make the survey at once. On about 2 October, Conrad replied that he had no funds and could not comply with the request.

At the moment McClelland received this piece of bad news from Washington, he also had a stroke of luck. Present with him was a competent engineer who grasped the problem at once. Augustus Canfield, captain of the Army Corps of Topographical Engineers, had graduated from West Point in 1822 and had served the next twelve years in the artillery. In 1834 he was made a brevet captain and staff assistant in the Corps of Topographical Engineers, and on 17 July 1838 he became a full captain. His wife was the former Mary Cass, daughter of the senator. Canfield was no stranger to the Sault area. In 1839 he had completed a survey of the Sault and a general plan for a canal. He had simplified Almy's design by reducing the number of locks from three to two, and he proposed to add a pier and a sand-catcher to the Lake Superior end of the canal.[20]

Without waiting for the approval of Colonel J. J. Abert, commander of the Corps of Topographical Engineers, Canfield sailed north to conduct a fresh survey, which began on 5 October. As he later explained to McClelland, he found it necessary to run three survey lines through the portage in order to chart the best possible canal route. He had to consider several important factors in locating the upper end of the route on Lake Superior. For safe navigation it had to be as far from the rapids as possible. To minimize the cost of the upper piers and cofferdam, the current must be minimal at the point selected. Finally, Canfield was pleased to note that the existing docks on the Lake Superior side would not be disturbed, and that business could be conducted as usual during construction.

With two exceptions Canfield confirmed his own design made in 1839. First, he moved the passing basins from the south side of the canal to the north. Since the canal towpath had to be on the south side to avoid the rapids, Canfield had made a foolish error in 1839 in placing the basins on the same side. No mule born could tow a sailing ship out of a south basin when the prevailing winds came from the west. The second exception was to shift the course of a canal a mere two degrees at the cove to avoid a sandbar in the St. Mary's River. Since the canal banks would be of solid earth or rock at this point, Canfield, to avoid a washout, made a minor—but only minor—violation of the rule that the canal route must not curve.[21]

Unfortunately, the two changes created a new problem that boded ill for the future. As Canfield noted, the center line of the canal passed 50 feet from the river bank at the cove. Since by law the canal must be 100 feet wide, the eastern passing basin (now moved to the north side of the canal) would extend into the cove. An embankment of earth might meet the situation, but any leak in the bank would cause serious trouble. If Canfield had realized the danger, he could easily have moved the basin farther west. To move the canal a major distance to the south was not a viable alternative, since this would have doubled its length and run it through the village.

Canfield included in his report several pages concerning such technical matters as sand-catching piers, lake fluctuations, and machinery requirements, but one fact became obvious. He could not make an accurate cost estimate because he could not probe the lock location with an iron rod to a depth greater than five feet; the ground was too cluttered with heavy boulders. Canfield was quite candid about this weakness in his report. Further, he admitted that his estimate of $15,000 for transportation of materials was a wild guess. At this time he had no idea where to get limestone for the locks, and limestone would be the major bulk item transported to the project.

Concerning the dimensions and drainage of the locks, Canfield made two important decisions: the first proved wise, but the second, unfortunately, did not. Anticipating increases in the length of Great Lakes ships, the engineer decided to exceed the requirements of the law when he specified the locks' dimensions. Congress had required that they measure at least 60 feet wide and no less than 250 feet long, but Canfield proposed to construct them 70 feet wide and 300 feet long. The exceeding of federal dimensions, since it was increased even more by the legislature, was the most vital decision in the early history of the Sault canal. It would govern ship construction on the Great Lakes for decades, just as the dimensions of the locks of the Panama Canal governed United States naval construction for many years. Further, the length of the ships governed cargo-carrying capacity. Canfield's decision, reinforced by the legislature, played an important role in Lake Superior economics until the completion of the Weitzel Lock in 1881.

For maintenance and repair there must be a way to drain the entire canal, and Canfield made a poor decision when he decided to meet the problem by constructing a caisson gate as near to Lake Superior as possible. The gate would be nothing more than a great, floating (when empty) watertight box. When not in use it would be pumped out and floated away to storage. When needed, it could be towed into place and sunk by refilling. It would then fit snugly between the canal sides and rest on the canal floor. In theory the mechanism was quite simple, but in practice it required such accurate masonry and carpentry that Canfield would have done better to order a simple guard gate.

Canfield estimated a total cost of $557,739.10, after allowing a 5 percent factor for contingencies. As it turned out, he would have been much closer to the actual cost if he had used a factor of 100 percent. Army engineers as well as their civilian counterparts have long had a reputation for underestimating the costs of proposed projects. In 1836 the House Ways and Means Committee censured army and civilian engineers for misleading Congress with low estimates, and in 1845 a friend of the Reading Railroad criticized the low cost estimates of a potential rival canal project and wrote: "It is difficult enough to get new projects requiring large investments, and to carry them out. . . . These sorts of projects will not bear any

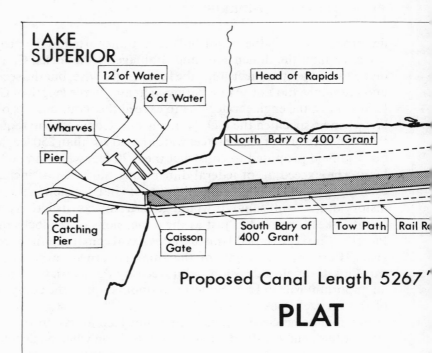

LAKE
SUPERIOR

12' of Water

6' of Water

Head of Rapids

Wharves

North Bdry of 400' Grant

Pier

Sand
Catching
Pier

Caisson
Gate

South Bdry of
400' Grant

Tow Path

Rail Ro

Proposed Canal Length 5267'

PLAT

PROFILE

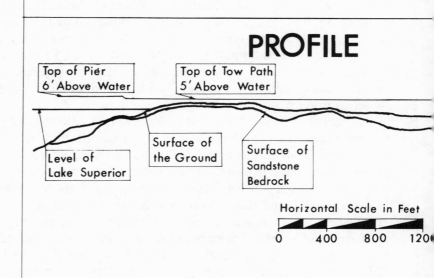

Top of Pier
6' Above Water

Top of Tow Path
5' Above Water

Level of
Lake Superior

Surface of
the Ground

Surface of
Sandstone
Bedrock

Horizontal Scale in Feet

0   400   800   120

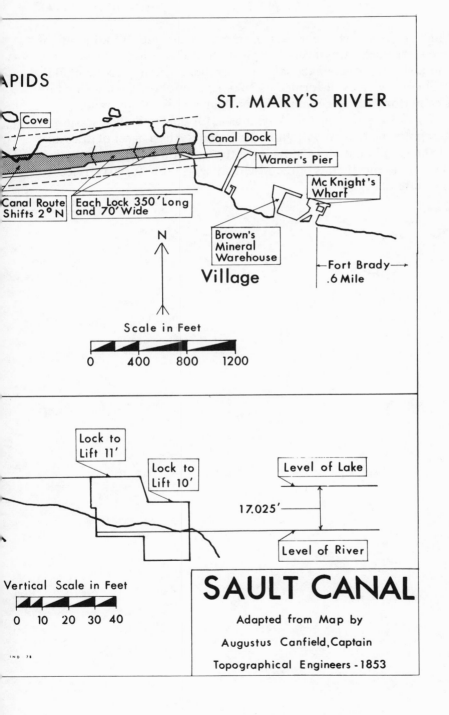

APIDS

Cove

ST. MARY'S RIVER

Canal Dock

Warner's Pier

McKnight's Wharf

Canal Route Shifts 2° N

Each Lock 350' Long and 70' Wide

Brown's Mineral Warehouse

N
↑

Village

←Fort Brady→
.6 Mile

Scale in Feet

0   400   800   1200

Lock to Lift 11'

Lock to Lift 10'

Level of Lake

17.025'

Level of River

Vertical Scale in Feet

0   10   20   30   40

SAULT CANAL

Adapted from Map by

Augustus Canfield, Captain

Topographical Engineers - 1853

IND 78

kind of discouragement, but on the contrary require all kinds of encouragement. Engineers must live; they, therefore, very naturally think it is fair to err on the safe side, for them." In this case Canfield's estimates were as ill-formed as Nichols's, but both men were quite straightforward in acknowledging their points of ignorance.[22]

When Cass returned to Washington for the lame-duck session of Congress, he carried with him, for Colonel Abert, a set of drawings of the canal made by Canfield. In the meantime Canfield received the unanimous thanks of the Michigan legislature for his services to the state.[23]

4 Legislation and a Contract

The development of plans and estimates for the canal project was one thing; ensuring its political survival was quite a different matter. Business and political rivalries were intense in Michigan in January 1853, and both would have a bearing on the canal contract.

Once it had become politically safe (or politically irrelevant) for him to do so, Lewis Cass pushed the canal bill through Congress. Then he stumped Michigan in behalf of canal supporter Robert McClelland. After the election the defeated candidate for governor, Whig mayor of Detroit Zachariah Chandler, blamed Cass for his loss, and the *Detroit Daily Advertiser* openly questioned whether Democrats could be trusted with the canal project.[1]

Business rivalries were no less threatening to the project. The moment the Michigan Central Railroad's attorney James Joy appeared on the Lansing scene in behalf of canal bidders, the identity of these bidders would be revealed. The Michigan Central had a natural set of enemies in the Midwest, the officers of the Michigan Southern. The two railroads were constantly at war until 1857, cutting rates, granting discounts, and fighting for business.[2]

In addition, there was no secret about the cooperation between the leaders of the Michigan Central and those of the about-to-be formed New York Central Railroad. John Murray Forbes and Erastus Corning had taken control of the Michigan Central in 1846, and Forbes had been elected president. If Corning were to complete his consolidation of the New York Central in the mid 1850s, the Michigan Central could serve as a feeder—a bleak prospect for supporters of the Michigan Southern.[3]

Several members of the Michigan legislature exhibited concern about the railroad situation before the session opened. When a few approached Corning, Joy advised him to reassure them and refer them to the good offices of Joy and Porter (Joy's partner) in Detroit. To further coordinate his activities in the East and the Midwest, Corning sent Harvey to Detroit with a letter of introduction to John W. Brooks, superintendent of the Michigan Central, and to Joy. He also sent some sound advice, suggesting that as little commotion as possible attend the matter. Corning did not want to attract attention.[4]

Despite the presence of Harvey, the critical figure at this stage of the canal project was James F. Joy. Joy had been born in New Hampshire, and had received his law degree from Harvard in 1835 and moved to Detroit. During the early 1840s he was a leader in the effort to sell the Michigan Central to private buyers. John Brooks recognized Joy's ability when that project succeeded and persuaded him to enter the railroad business as general counsel of the Michigan Central. The railroad proved to be a hard school for the man described by Forbes as a "keen, clever energetic, Western lawyer." For the next years the principal goal of the Michigan Central was to obtain access to Chicago. Accomplishing it meant charter battles in the legislatures of Indiana and Illinois, with the Michigan Southern fighting every inch of the way. Finally Joy and Brooks solved the problem by purchasing control of the New Albany and Salem Railroad in Indiana, the chief asset of which consisted of a vague charter. Thus the Michigan Central reached Chicago. In 1853 Joy, at forty-two, was a veteran of legislative struggles, and already he and Brooks were casting their eyes farther west.[5]

Canal interests were well represented when the Michigan legislature assembled in January 1853. Herman B. Ely attended as the representative of Chippewa County and the Sault. Judge William A. Burt had secured election from Macomb County, and his was a name to reckon with. In 1844 he led the party that had discovered iron ore in what would become known as the Marquette range. Following this discovery, he had invented the solar compass, an invaluable instrument for surveying in iron fields. In the preceding October he had assisted Canfield in the canal survey. Now he would be chairman of the Committee on Internal Improvements of the Michigan House of Representatives. Serving with Burt on this committee was Orrin Poppleton, an advocate of long canal locks.

Another member who kept Joy informed of legislative proceedings when the attorney was absent from Lansing was Deodatus Whitwood.[6]

On the evening of 29 December 1852, friends of the canal project held a meeting in Detroit with John Burt, a son of the judge, to see what general agreements could be reached in order to guide the legislature. From the session the group developed a consensus. The canal locks were to be as long as possible and at least sixty feet wide. A state commission should be appointed with the power to enter into contracts, appoint engineers, and inspect the finished project. The only disagreement arose over the matter of taxing the lands to be granted to the canal builders. One group held that the land should be taxed at once so that the tax burden would not fall unfairly on non-canal lands. Another group feared that if the lands were not tax-exempt for a least a limited period, as was the usual procedure in the sale or grant of all public lands, the state might have trouble finding anyone willing to build the canal. This issue would have to be settled by the legislature.[7]

The following days were hectic ones for Joy. He agreed to help steer a canal bill favorable to the Corning interests through the legislature, but he would not invest in the project for himself or his friends. Harvey offered Joy a draft of a canal bill, which Joy amended for submission in Lansing. The little group in Detroit then decided on a division of labor: Brooks was to go east as soon as possible to consult with Corning on engineering details, Joy departed for Lansing with the drafted bill, and Harvey remained in Detroit. It was not intended that Joy linger in Lansing. The Illinois legislature was also in session, and the Michigan Central group had four measures pending in Springfield that required his attention. In Michigan, in addition to the canal problem, Brooks wanted an amendment passed to the Michigan Central charter; moreover, Whitwood probably needed the lawyer's guidance. Joy must have wished at times that he were twins, but his experience was typical of the entire canal project, in which a few men were trying to reach a number of goals at the same time.[8]

Harvey did not relish his share of the duties and complained to Corning. In Harvey's own words, the friends of the canal project feared that his presence in Lansing might have an "injurious tendency" on the members of the legislature. Apparently Joy and

Brooks did not share the confidence in the bumptious young man
that Corning and Fairbanks had displayed. Harvey did have the
opportunity to consult with shipowner Eber Ward and learned from
Ward that Ohio contractors would bid on the canal project. Ward
indicated that he favored the Corning group, and the latter thus
gained another valuable ally.[9]

Finally Joy summoned Harvey to Lansing with the understand-
ing that the young man would keep out of sight. Rumors of fat
profits to be made on the canal project circulated in the state capital.
There were fears that speculators might seize the land without
building the canal. Some legislators proposed so many restrictions
and conditions in the canal contract as to make the project almost
impossible. Joy, who was familiar with such situations, did not want
Harvey to interfere. By 20 January he succeeded in having the canal
bill introduced in the Michigan House.[10]

The legislature had to make the final decision with regard to the
length of the locks. Canfield had proposed to exceed federal
requirements by building 300-foot locks. Others, including Brown
at the Sault, held out for 350 feet. This figure upset Eber Ward, who
pointed out to William Burt that obstructions in the St. Mary's
River would restrict the class of steamers anyway. Ward thought
that 260 feet would be an adequate length—and for *his* ships it
would have been. Brown, anticipating the dispute, had warned that
only second-class steamers could use the shorter locks. He averred
that ships of lake size needed room and should not be permitted to
bang against timber gates as Erie Canal barges sometimes did. A
conference committee of the legislature succeeded in ironing out the
last of these differences on 2 February, and McClelland signed the
bill on 5 February. The locks would be 350 feet in length.[11]

The legislature made no attempt to prescribe details of the canal
other than to specify that the locks must be 350 feet long and 70 feet
wide. Federal law set the depth at 12 feet. As was standard practice
by the 1850s, the lawmakers also created a five-man commission
whose members, along with a state engineer, would have
considerable authority. The commissioners and the engineer were to
be appointed by the governor with the consent of the state senate.
They would have "the entire and absolute control of the
construction of said canal." Since it was hardly expected that the
entire five-member board would move to the Sault for two years, the

real authority under the law would be vested in the state engineer.

Not only was the commission authorized to receive proposals for the canal's construction and to enter into contracts; it was also obliged to consider the responsibility of the persons offering to contract. Here the Corning group held a decided advantage. Security for performance was required. The contractors were to defray the necessary expenses of the commissioners and the salaries and expenses of the state engineer and his assistants. The state would then pay the commissioners and the engineers.

The legislature agreed with Harvey's contention that the canal could and should be completed in two years, whereas Congress had permitted ten. The contracting party would be permitted to subcontract any part of the work it wished, but it was still responsible for completion in two years. Failure to complete would throw the contractor on the mercy of a future legislature. Although such a time limit would serve to discourage the fainthearted, it would also test Harvey severely. He would soon have to prove his own estimate or bring others down with him.

The governor was authorized to appoint agents to select the 750,000 acres required for the project. Most vital to the Corning interests was the provision granting to the contracting party the right to nominate such agents. The governor must appoint those recommended if he considered them qualified. Thus, if the governor was willing, the contracting party could nominate its own friends and, in effect, select the land it would receive. This was the only way the system could work. The state could not grant alternate sections along a canal only one mile long. On the other hand, no responsible party would enter into the agreement if some disinterested official could award 750,000 acres of swamp. The Michigan legislature decided not to relinquish the land until the project was completed, although federal law would have permitted Michigan to do so. Thus the contracting party would have to depend upon its own financial resources for the entire two-year period.[12]

The law did not mention the tax status of the grant land, so Joy had more work to do in Lansing. One week later the legislature passed the desired supplementary act. The grant lands would be exempt from taxation for a period of five years, the standard provision with federal lands. If the contractors should sell the land within five years, then it would be taxed at once. The amount lost from this policy of exemption would be charged to the general fund. However, the supplementary act also provided that the general fund be reimbursed from the canal tolls for this loss. Thus the burden of the loss would fall upon those who would gain the most from the canal, the Great Lakes shipping men.[13]

With this favorable legislation passed, Joy could turn to other matters. Soon after the passage of the Michigan laws, Brooks and Corning's partner, Gilbert C. Davidson, were elected to the board of directors of the Chicago and Aurora Railroad; Joy was elected president. In the preceding year Joy, with the backing of Corning and Fairbanks, had struggled to gain control of the Central Military Tract Railroad. This fight was successfully concluded in August 1852, and the railroad combination that would be called the Chicago, Burlington, and Quincy began to take shape under Joy's legal guidance. Two months after the passage of the canal bills in Michigan, the New York legislature granted the necessary measure to create the New York Central Railroad. Corning, who held a majority of the proxies, had personally taken charge of the lobby in Albany, and on 6 July 1853 the stockholders elected him president. Thus, in the highly critical months of 1853, several of the canal principals could give only a portion of their time to canal problems.[14]

Harvey was confident of success as he left Michigan after the passage of the laws. He traveled to Utica, New York, for another consultation with Nichols, then to Albany to see Corning, and finally to St. Johnsbury to visit his original employer, Erastus Fairbanks. By this time Harvey had lost all interest in selling scales, but it was necessary for the eastern canal backers, including Fairbanks, to agree upon the specific form of their proposal.[15]

Although the canal commission would receive bids until 1 April, by the middle of March Brooks began to worry. He warned Corning that the bids were beginning to arrive in Detroit, one of them postmarked Pittsburgh. Brooks, obviously aided by an informer, assumed that the bid came from one of the copper interests. He urged Corning to send a representative to Detroit before the opening of the bids.[16]

Joy, more confident, predicted victory eight days before the Corning group presented its proposal and four days before he had even seen the proposal in its final form. Harvey reported by wire that all the eastern negotiations were completed and that he was on the way back to Detroit with the papers. On 30 March the canal commission held a meeting in Detroit attended by Brooks, who noted the presence of Whig politician Jacob Howard. Correctly identifying Howard as an enemy of the Corning group, Brooks realized that he would need Joy's help with the commission. He asked Joy to return from Chicago at once, reminding him that bids had to be presented by noon of the following day.[17]

Joy and Harvey presented the proposal to the commission before the deadline. For the completion of the canal, the Corning group asked for the maximum payment that the law permitted, the entire 750,000 acres tax-exempt for five years. There was no reason for them to do otherwise, for the state of Michigan would gain nothing by bargaining. Any land not used for the building of the canal would revert to the public domain under federal law. The state expected to recoup its tax losses from the canal tolls.

So successful had Joy been in dealing with the commission that several sources independently predicted victory for the Corning proposal. One was the *Detroit Free Press*, which announced—on the day before the commission opened the bids—the awarding of the contract to the Corning interests and concluded, "We may, therefore, look upon the completion of the canal within two years as a FIXED FACT." Another was Captain Canfield, who knew on 4 April that he was to be far more than an observer in the undertaking and reported to Colonel Abert that the Corning group would probably get the contract. Canfield, newly appointed engineer for the state of Michigan, wrote that the commission had been in session all of 4 April considering eight bids. He listed the names of Corning's associates, calling "all of them half million men." Since the Michigan law required the commission to consider the reputation and reliability of the bidders, Canfield had put his finger on the source of Corning's strength and Joy's optimism. He concluded to Abert, "If they take the contract it makes certain that the work will be done in a most satisfactory manner."[18]

The commission's decision, therefore, was hardly surprising. On 5 April it awarded the contract to the Corning group. The result was a new flurry of activity in Michigan and Albany. The announcement of the award did not automatically bring about the signing of the contract, and the opposition of Corning's enemies now became a public matter. Edwin C. Litchfield of the Michigan Southern Railroad, with his attorney Jacob Howard, obtained injunctions in Ann Arbor, Jackson, and Detroit against the awarding of the contract. Litchfield had been an unsuccessful bidder, and he was obviously determined to harass the Corning group with his charge of corruption. Corning's friend Frederick Bronson called the injunctions "all moonshine" and correctly pointed out that the Litchfield group was actually helping Corning without realizing it. Although the contract was dated 5 April 1853, the two-year construction period would not begin until it had actually been signed and approved by Michigan's new governor, Andrew Parsons. The delay would give Harvey some extra time; it remained to be seen if he would take full advantage of it.[19]

Harvey's first concern was the land grant. Sault editor J. Venen Brown had warned him that there might be a land rush in the Upper Peninsula as soon as the navigation season opened in 1853, and that the company had better be ready to move fast. In a letter undated, unsigned, and headed, "Read and Burn," Brown admitted that his paper was suffering financially; he therefore proposed a deal. He would look after the Corning group's land interests and give the project favorable publicity if Harvey could find some way of offering compensation. Seeing an opportunity to gain an advantage over other land-seekers, Harvey decided to take advantage of the dubious offer. He boarded the steamship *Albany* and headed north as soon as the decision of the commission had been announced. With him he took a certificate, signed by Governor Parsons on 5 April, making him a canal land agent.[20]

Harvey was also concerned with obtaining a source of high-grade limestone for the facing of the canal locks. Brown assured him that he owned such land on Lime Island and knew of other suitable deposits on Drummond's Island. Both locations were within forty miles of the Sault. Harvey took with him a land warrant so that he might purchase these sites outright. As he had anticipated, however, the St. Mary's River was still jammed with ice, and the *Albany* could steam no closer to the Sault and its land office than forty miles. Rejecting the hazardous overland hike, Harvey forwarded by messenger a number of documents and a letter of instruction to Brown. He ordered Brown to file in behalf of the Corning group for as much as he could of the best mineral land available, including property contiguous to all operating mines near Lake Gogebic, 5,000 acres at the mouth of the Chocolay River, land near the iron fields at Marquette, and "Jackson's Iron Mountain." Harvey also forwarded the land warrant, instructing Brown to purchase the limestone sources. To support Brown in these ventures, Harvey forwarded his certificate of appointment as land agent, as well as a letter deputizing Brown as a canal land agent.[21]

It was probable that Brown realized at once the illegality of the last document. Harvey had no authority to appoint land agents; only the governor could do so. At any rate, Brown acted swiftly and filed for the mineral lands in behalf of the Corning group. The legality of this move would be a matter for others to worry about.

The land warrant posed a different problem. Brown had decided to purchase the mineral lands in his own and Harvey's name. Having conducted a search for limestone, however, on 10 May he bought four lots on Drummond's Island in his name alone! He later explained accurately to Harvey that the deposits of limestone on Lime Island were not suitable for the project and that he did not want to waste Harvey's warrant on useless land. In June the unsuspecting Harvey placed Brown on his payroll at a salary of $2,000 per year, retroactive to 1 January 1853. When he left the St. Mary's River in April to return to Detroit, Harvey was satisfied that he had beaten the land-hungry speculators. Not the least worried about Brown, he reported to Corning, "Everything relating to the canal enterprise here seems to be in the best possible shape."[22]

Harvey then prepared to go east once again. Considering that nothing had been done in Detroit to prepare for the actual digging of the canal, he was headed in the wrong direction. He was no longer needed in the East, where men more competent than he were available to deal with the New York legislature and the details of organizing a company. His post instead should have been Detroit. Since the navigation season usually opened in early May, he should by then have had an advance crew of hundreds equipped with tools and ready to go to the Sault. These could be followed by as many as 1,000 men by 1 July. Such preparation would have taken much organizing in Detroit in April, yet Harvey elected to be elsewhere. It would seem that he failed to grasp the magnitude of the task ahead.

The Litchfield injunctions forced a minor change in Corning's plans. Instead of waiting for a signed contract with the State of

Michigan, he would have to obtain a charter in Albany before the New York legislature adjourned. That Corning proceeded to do this without delay was a good indication of his opinion of the injunctions.

There were a number of reasons why Corning in April 1853 could obtain almost anything he wanted from his legislature. At that time William Marcy was serving his second month as secretary of state, with jobs to fill. Corning and Marcy were on friendly terms, and John V. L. Pruyn, Corning's associate, had served as intermediary between Pierce and Marcy before Pierce had selected his secretary of state. As a result Corning found his mail filled with requests for federal jobs. For the time being he was in a favored position in the New York Democratic party.[23]

Nor would Corning have any difficulty with the Whig opposition. With Fillmore in retirement, Thurlow Weed and his associates led the party. Weed could hardly have blocked the completion of a Sault canal, since he had been strongly advocating one in his own newspaper since 1847. Further, in spite of political rivalry, Corning and Weed were personal friends. Also helping Corning was the fact that both New York's Whig senators had voted for the canal bill in Congress. Whig editor Horace Greeley's favorable stand on the matter was well known. The Whigs were hardly in a position to reverse themselves, especially when the matter did not directly concern New York. Thus Corning obtained his canal charter law, just as ten days earlier he had won the New York Central charter from the same legislature. Harvey, in Albany, notified Joy.[24]

The act of the New York legislature was simple enough, and for the first time the Corning group had an official name. Their organization was to be called "The St. Mary's Falls Ship Canal Company."[25] It was created for only two purposes: to enter into a contract with the State of Michigan to build the canal, and to facilitate the "taking, holding, improving, selling, and conveying the . . . lands as granted." The capital stock issue of the corporation was set at $400,000, with the directors at liberty to increase the issue to $1,000,000 at a later date. Individual shares were to have a par value of $100, and the sum of $5 per share must be paid at the time of the subscription for the stock. As soon as the capital stock had been subscribed, the company could elect a board of directors and officers; and, at the time of organizing, the company must have a minimum of $20,000 available to begin construction.

The law called for seven directors to hold office for one year as elected by the stockholders. Notices of the annual meeting must be placed in a newspaper in New York City and in the State of Michigan. The directors had the authority to issue further calls on the stock until all the stock subscribed for had been paid in full. Failure to meet such a call carried the penalty of forfeiture of the stock and all payments made to date. The law set a limit on bonded indebtedness at $250,000.[26]

While Corning was overseeing the law's passage in Albany, Joy, on railroad business in Chicago, was attempting to direct his Detroit law partner in clearing up the vexatious injunctions. The canal contract was held in the safe of the Michigan Central Railroad in Detroit, pending the end of harassment. On 28 April, Joy ordered Porter to get the Detroit injunction dissolved. Then, "without a word being said to anyone about it," Deodatus Whitwood was to take a copy of the dissolving order and the contract to Lansing for the approval of the governor. Joy emphasized that no one in Detroit must know where Whitwood had gone or for what purpose. Upon learning that Harvey had returned to Detroit, Joy ordered him to help Porter; but in spite of their efforts, the Detroit enemies of the canal were able to obtain a delay.[27]

The hearing on the Jackson injunction came next, and Joy could wire Corning that at least one of the nuisances had been eliminated. He then instructed Porter to take the contract to Michigan canal commissioners Shubael Conant and Henry Ledyard for their signatures, since these two men happened to live in Detroit. Whitwood would then take the papers to Lansing. Again Joy was frustrated, however; Brooks wrote in exasperation that the commissioners would not execute the contract until all the injunctions had been dissolved. Brooks suggested that the canal commissioners be persuaded instead to write a letter requesting the company to begin the project. It was his opinion that such a letter would constitute a contract and would "give us all courage at once."[28]

Corning had courage enough for everybody. Perhaps he remembered the words of James Joy as the Michigan Central fought to gain entry into Chicago: "These are times when bold action is the only safe action." In any case, he proceeded with the financing and

organizing of his company as if the injunctions did not exist. The
stockholders must meet in New York City. The company must hire
an engineer. Brooks, who objected to certain engineering
specifications and had advanced his own plan for financing the
company, must be dealt with. Forbes and Joy must be included on
the team. Corning had to attend to all these matters in April, May,
June, and July 1853, and these were also the months of the
formation of the New York Central. John V. L. Pruyn estimated the
combined values of the railroads involved in the merger to be in
excess of $30,000,000. Corning could hardly give his first attention
to canal matters.[29]

It had been Corning's intention that the first and most important
stockholders' meeting be held on 10 May. But Harvey, who should
have been quite aware of the stipulations of the New York law, had
neglected to insert the required notice in a Michigan newspaper
before leaving Detroit for Albany. Corning assumed that the notice
had been published; his first intimation of the slip came when
Brooks rushed a newspaper notice to Albany for his signature.
Brooks was more alert than Harvey, and he wanted to avoid a new
legal tangle in Detroit. The delay forced Corning to reschedule the
meeting, first for 12 May and then for 14 May. The result was a
growl from St. Johnsbury. Governor Fairbanks had canceled his
appointments for 10 May in order to go to the meeting; now he
wanted to know the reason for its postponement. Further
complicating matters was the illness of Pruyn, who would look after
such matters in the future with meticulous care. Altogether, it was
hardly an auspicious beginning.[30]

Meanwhile, Corning continued his efforts to organize the new
company. He managed to persuade Forbes to take a financial
interest in the project, and in turn Forbes agreed to approach
Nathaniel Thayer, a major stockholder in the Michigan Central and
New York Central railroads. Corning then asked Forbes to be a
director of the Canal Company. The request brought the reluctant
reply, "It is inconvenient to go on but I will if you consider it
important." Corning considered it important, and on the back of
Forbes's telegram he wrote seven names: J. W. Brooks, James F.
Joy, Erastus Fairbanks, John M. Forbes, John F. Seymour, E.
Corning, and John V. L. Pruyn. Joy had once refused to take a
financial interest in the canal project; but Corning had managed to

convert him in four months, and he now subscribed for 312 shares. Brooks subscribed for 400 shares, an enormous number for a railroad superintendent, although his salary was unusually high. (He apparently had some peculiar ideas on how to finance the project so as to minimize the demands on the Brooks bank account.) Corning was helped in the subscription drive by the general condition of the railroad stock market in 1853. Forbes considered the market bearish and the western situation overdeveloped, but business editor Henry Varnum Poor noted that western railroad stocks were selling well above par. Certainly there were fewer stock bargains in 1853 than there had been in 1850. At any rate, Corning's efforts produced the board of directors he wanted. When the stockholders finally met in the offices of Duncan, Sherman & Company on 14 May, they elected the seven men whose names Corning had written on the back of Forbes's telegram. The directors then elected Corning president, Brooks vice-president, and Pruyn secretary-treasurer. Finally, upon a motion of Forbes, seconded by Seymour, the directors elected Harvey the general agent of the Canal Company with broad executive powers.[31]

With the company organized and $20,000 in its till (and more to come in sooner than Brooks anticipated), Harvey might have been expected to head for the Sault with an advance working crew within hours of the adjournment of the meeting. He had already wasted enough time in Albany watching Corning handle the New York legislature. Nor were the injunctions an excuse for delay; they were obviously a farce, and Corning enterprises did not always stand upon ceremony in such matters. For example, Pruyn had altered the rate structure of the Utica and Schenectady Railroad on instructions from Corning four days before the signing of the New York Central merger agreement, although, strictly speaking, he had no right to do so. Nevertheless, Harvey continued to waste valuable time by proceeding to New England to negotiate loans for Joy and Porter. Brooks too was badly out of position, but he had a good excuse. Immediately after the stockholders meeting, he had undergone surgery in Boston, and he was now recovering under the watchful eye of Forbes. The Boston financier warned Corning that Brooks "needs some relief which we must contrive and manage for him or he will break down." He was right, but Brooks's real ordeal was still to come. The best thing that Corning could have done for

Brooks would have been to get Harvey to attend to business in 1853. This he failed to do, although Harvey did return to Albany in time to consult with Corning and Nichols after the latter had consented to serve as engineer for the Canal Company.[32]

In giving Harvey a large measure of authority over the canal project, to say nothing of acquiescing to his travels, Corning was following a procedure born of necessity. He was, among other things, a highly successful merchant. Buying and selling had given him the financial base from which to branch out into railroading, canal building, and land speculation. Like all successful merchants of the era, he had to pay strict attention to the minute details of business. Success, however, brought the problem of distance and the necessity of making firm commitments and establishing authority many miles from Albany. Communications were often difficult, and telegraph messages were not always private. To add to the difficulty, Corning was forced to spend a great part of his life walking with the aid of crutches as a result of a childhood hip injury.

Corning solved the problem by using rare judgment in his choice of partners and associates. These were given considerable authority, and as a rule they held Corning in high esteem. He was also willing to intercede with associates over whom he had no direct authority. In 1847 Corning recognized Brooks's difficult position as superintendent of the Michigan Central while Forbes ran the railroad from a desk in Boston. Corning told Brooks that he considered him to be the "responsible agent" of the railroad and advised him to demand more authority from Forbes. Brooks, who was in his late twenties at the time, must have appreciated this word of confidence.[33]

With Harvey, therefore, Corning followed a well-established practice that usually worked for him. As the last of the injunctions was dissolved, it remained to be seen if this time Corning's—and Fairbanks's—judgment was as sound as usual. Governor Parsons approved the contract on 19 May. Thus 19 May 1855 became the target date for the completion of the canal and a cardinal date in the lives of Corning and his associates.[34]

5 Complacency 1853

On 3 June the advance party finally embarked for the Sault on the steamboat *Albany*. Since navigation had opened in the first week of May, Harvey had wasted one month of valuable time. On board the *Albany* were Harvey, Canfield, and two newcomers to the project, Major James L. Glenn and Charles W. Chapel. Glenn was an early resident and prominent citizen of Cass County, Michigan, who had served as sheriff and state representative in the 1840s. Educated as a civil engineer, he was appointed to a commission to plan and survey Lansing and to erect a statehouse in 1847. He had had no experience in canal construction when, in 1853, he was made assistant state engineer, responsible to Canfield and the canal commission. Chapel, a resident of Utica, Michigan, had been the co-owner of a flour mill. His only experience with "canal problems" had been his successful lawsuit against the State of Michigan for the diversion of his water supply. In 1852 he employed Joy and Porter as legal counsel, and he probably came to the attention of the canal company through Joy. The company hired him to be superintendent of excavation, a job that would not be very demanding as long as he had adequate manpower and tools. With the party sailed about one hundred workmen.[1]

Of all the people aboard the *Albany*, Canfield was in the most unusual position. All the others knew that he was now the chief engineer for the state and were aware of his authority under the canal law. They assumed that he would play a passive role, objecting only if the specifications were violated or poor workmanship displayed. What they probably did not know was that Canfield was under direct orders from Colonel Abert to "superintend the construction of the canal at Saut Ste. Marie," and sooner or later he might exert executive authority to carry out Abert's orders. It was a difficult situation, not helped by the fact that Canfield wore several hats and was trying to do a number of jobs at once. He had surveyed and designed the canal, and now, as state engineer and superintendent of canal construction, he would have to approve his own handiwork. In addition, he was directing the dredging of Lake St. Clair, 400 miles away at the foot of Lake Huron, where he had left his draftsman in charge. Finally, he had general supervision of all lighthouses and harbor work on Lake Superior. Such an overload was Canfield's reward for exceptional ability and experience.[2]

The *Albany* docked at the Sault on 6 June, and preliminary work began at once. It would first be necessary to erect a number of rough shanties to house the work force, another task that should have been done in May. The construction took almost two weeks; meanwhile the engineers scoured the countryside for limestone. On 11 June the steamship *London* arrived from Detroit with 40,000 feet of lumber, cattle and carts, and twenty-four workmen, including twelve carpenters. Still to come were wheelbarrows, picks, shovels, and crowbars from Albany.[3]

If Sault editor Brown realized the significance of the tool shortage he reported, he refrained from comment. Every week his newspaper carried columns of advertising for Detroit stores and warehouses that would probably stock all the equipment needed at the Sault, since these same tools were essential to the mining industry. If they could be brought to the Sault from Detroit in three or four days, why wait for delivery from Albany, 700 miles away?

Though Brown did not know it, Corning was implementing another of his standard practices. He would serve as president of the Canal Company without salary, but all the iron tools and supplies must be bought at his own Albany warehouses and foundry, enabling him to make a good profit, though not an exorbitant one. His iron foundary, already the major supplier for the Michigan Central and the Utica and Schenectady Railroads, was about to assume a similar responsibility for the New York Central as well. In the 1850s this was considered legitimate business practice; moreover, the general quality of Corning's merchandise was excellent. He was building for his own future, not planning to dump a shoddy railroad on someone else. The practice would not come into question until the 1870s, after a number of shoddy railroads *had* been peddled, and by 1875 it would be roundly condemned. In the case of the canal, however, the problem was timing rather than inferior merchandise. Knowing that the tools must come from Albany, Harvey should have made arrangements in April and May.[4]

Slowly, much too slowly, the labor force built up at the Sault. By the end of June, there were only 232 men, including supervisors, engineers, and a housekeeping crew. July passed with the number climbing to 340. In the month of August, 115 more men arrived, but in September only 4 new hands were added. On 22 September, Harvey reported in round numbers the allocation of his work force. He had 300 men in the excavation, 40 carpenters and helpers next to the lock pits, 45 lumbermen in the forests, and 35 men in a nearby quarry. The numbers were woefully inadequate, yet on 23 August, Harvey reported excellent progress.[5]

Had Harvey grasped the magnitude of the task before him, the application of the most elementary mathematics would have thrown him into shock. On 1 August, Brooks reported from Detroit that 188,000 cubic yards of excavation remained to be done. It needed only a simple equation to point out the danger ahead:

$$\frac{\text{percent of excavation completed}}{\text{percent of excavation remaining}} = \frac{\text{man-days of work completed}}{\text{man-days of work remaining}}$$

Harvey knew both factors on the left side of the equation; he knew, or could establish from his pay records, the man-days completed; he knew how many construction days remained to complete the contract, allowing a factor for inclement weather. He needed only to solve the equation to form a good estimate of his manpower requirement—but apparently Brooks solved it for him. Editor Brown could marvel at the four "monstrous cranes" in operation, but he did not know that Canfield had recommended ten for the lock pits alone. Brown began to use the ominous word "granite" as early as 2 July, when Harvey ordered granite boulders drilled so that they could be blasted to celebrate the nation's birthday. It was a grand but empty gesture. What was needed was more manpower.[6]

The situation would not alarm Brooks until September, when he was to rush more men to the work site from Detroit. Despite difficulties in recruitment, in the ten days prior to 5 November he

sent about 350 men to Harvey, but by that time the work season was
nearly over. Moreover, competition for labor in the Upper
Peninsula was keen. Mineowners were looking for men who might
be willing to spend the winter working in the copper fields, and they
were not above hiring canal men traveling on the boats between
Detroit and the Sault, even men whose fare the Canal Company had
paid. At the same time, however, the work force in the United States
was growing. In 1852 more than 360,000 people emigrated from the
British Isles, with above 80 percent coming to the United States, a
migration that continued until the panic of 1857. The wave of
German immigrants, numbering 215,000 in 1854 alone, was about
to reach its crest. A labor supply was available, but the Canal
Company would have to work to get it.[7]

Low wages and poor morale were the chief deterrents to
maintaining an adequate work force. Harvey offered standard
wages for extra-long work days. The men who boarded with the
company, as most did, received $20 a month; day laborers earned
$1.10 per day. In comparison Corning paid his labor on the New
York Central about $1 per day after the general wage reduction of
1857. Years earlier, laborers on the Erie Canal had received from $8
to $12 per month. True, the Sault Canal Company fed and sheltered
most of its men, but many years later Harvey estimated the cost of
boarding the men at only 19¢ a day per man. (Brooks estimated the
cost at 33¢.) Men who did not live and board in the company's
shanties could buy supplies through the company store, where
Harvey undersold the local merchants, much to their displeasure. A
barrel of flour, for example, cost $10 on the local Sault market, and
Harvey sold it for $8. Brooks, Corning, and Fairbanks would not
have tolerated gouging of workers at the company store, an ugly
practice that began in a later era. The chief morale problems were
twofold. First, the company expected its men to work eleven and a
half hours a day at a time when the standard work day was ten
hours. Then, after a month of monotonous toil, the workers had
nothing on which to spend their wages except whiskey. Thus the
labor force dribbled in slowly until Brooks saw the urgent need for
more men. By October masons were reporting in squads of two or
three, and those skilled in their trade were making $3 per day while
those less skilled received $2.50.[8]

Other problems beset Harvey, among them bookkeeping

difficulties. He had neglected to secure the services of a bookkeeper until it was too late for him to attend to the matter himself. He then asked Fairbanks to get the address of a man in Pittsburgh who might do, and Fairbanks discovered that no such person existed. Fairbanks then called upon Corning for help. Eventually C. E. Bigelow took the job and reported on 1 August that the company books at the Sault were in such disorder that he could not vouch for the accuracy of what he was doing. By that time the company had already spent over $36,000. Harvey's careless habits with money had also gotten him into trouble with Pruyn, the company's secretary-treasurer. Before leaving for the Sault, Harvey had drawn a sight draft on Pruyn for $10,000, and Pruyn did not know what to do with it. He complained to Corning that "these matters should not be done in this loose way," and suggested that in the future Brooks countersign Harvey's drafts, a suggestion that would not find favor with Harvey.[9]

The men had been at work for barely two months when they decided that the work day was too long for the money received. On 1 August the labor force went on strike, demanding that the Canal Company adopt the standard ten-hour day or increase the wages by $6 a month for the eleven and one-half hour day. However, they quickly learned that when they were boarded by their employer and lived in his shanties, they acquired certain disadvantages in a strike. Harvey later wrote, "Feeling that to seccumb [sic] to such a movement was to entail a series of strikes and compromises on the progress of the work, I refused mildly but firmly to change the Co. terms whatever,—stopped their monthly pay and *removed the deposits*' [sic] of food and bed clothing from the shanties before the succeeding meal." The men could work or starve. Eighty opted for the first choice the following morning. Harvey watched over the workers, as the strikers threatened to stone them. After an hour or so he was satisfied, and ordered the work stopped and the men fed for the first time in twenty-four hours. By the end of the day, nearly all were back in the excavation. According to Harvey, "The main cause was the influence of the grog shop keepers who disliked the temperance rules of the Co. one of whom I had arrested, and kept in jail till he asked forgiveness with due humility." Another day and half had been lost.[10]

As the summer passed, Brooks, in Detroit, was not yet aware that the project was in serious trouble. His railroad responsibilities did not permit him to go to the Sault until the second week in August, so for the most part he had to rely on the enthusiastic reports from Harvey. Harvey needed a stream tug, and Brooks bought him the *Dart*. Harvey also requested a small fleet of scows to haul lumber. Brooks tried to purchase them "ready made" from the Ohio Canal at Cleveland and expressed annoyance to Corning that he had not been warned in advance that the scows would be needed. On 1 August, encouraged by Harvey's optimism, Brooks told Corning that 100,000 cubic yards of earth and rock would be excavated in the next four months.[11]

In early July, Harvey had decided to subcontract the major task of providing the heavy timber and planking for the lock floors, gates, caisson gate, piers, and wharves. By the time the local lumbermen had submitted their bids, July was over. Upon opening the bids of 1 August, Harvey discovered that no one had attempted to bid on the entire lumber requirement. It should have been a warning to him, for the entire job was too great an undertaking for any one of the experienced men of the Upper Peninsula. Characteristically, Harvey decided that the Canal Company could provide its own heavy timber "at a saving of 3%" (hence the sudden need for the scows). Only the planking would be subcontracted, at a rate of $11.50 per thousand feet of pine and $16 per thousand feet of oak. Harvey reported that he had located a fine stand of pine and had at once procured it for the company.[12]

Meanwhile, land problems began to plague the Canal Company as a result of Harvey's illegal and impetuous delegation of authority in April. The land that Brown had reserved for the company on 27 April had suddenly been returned to the public domain and then immediately reclaimed by Harvey on 21 June. It was a rather clear admission on Harvey's part that the Brown claims might not be valid. But what of the rights of those who had entered the canal lands under the assumption that Brown had acted without authority? A cry of protest arose from several with land interests in the Upper Peninsula, led by State Representative Abner Sherman, and he and his friends appealed to Washington. The secretary of the interior was none other than former Michigan governor Robert McClelland, a friend of the canal project; he ruled in favor of the Canal Company on 27 January 1854. The Brown claims as reentered by Harvey were sustained, but the company now had a bitter enemy in Sherman.[13]

As the construction season approached its end, it was time for the Canal Company directors to take stock of the progress made. As a result of his several visits to the Sault, Brooks had spurred Harvey into increased activity and had sent him additional workers. By the middle of August, Harvey had assigned all available labor to the lock pits. Excavating the pits was vital to the time schedule, since the flooring timber could not be put in place until the excavation was completed. In turn, the masonry work could not commence until the flooring was in, nor could it continue after the first heavy frost of winter. Harvey should have concentrated on lock excavation in June to the exclusion of everything else except dock work. The rest of the canal, a simple ditch, could be excavated later while the masons were at work in the locks. Again Harvey had failed to plan ahead.[14]

Canfield tried to improve the situation by designing and constructing a bailing wheel powered by the water of the rapids. By keeping the locks reasonably dry, this released men from the onerous task of pumping for more important work. Canfield, with his numerous obligations, was forced to spend part of his time supervising the St. Clair dredging project, but even while in Detroit he worked on models of canal locks. He fell ill in July, and at the end of the summer reported, "I never in my life was so busy as I am just at this time."[15]

Harvey did not realize it, but in spite of all his problems he was having good luck with the weather. Although at least some rain fell on half the days in June, the weather for the next four months was excellent for construction work. The highest temperature recorded in Fort Brady in July was 81 degrees; in August, 86. It rained only fifteen times during these important sixty-two days. Fall was mild, and the *Dart* was able to haul timber up the St. Mary's River until 19 December. The men on the project remained in good health.[16]

Nevertheless, Nichols made the first discouraging report from the Sault on 15 September, with a warning that the work might not be completed on time. He noted that about one-seventh of the time allotted had passed and that about two-sevenths, or 64,000 cubic yards, of excavation had been completed. However, the remaining excavation would be far more difficult and expensive. Much would

be in rock, which must be lifted greater distances as the work
progressed. Furthermore, the job would certainly be slowed down
by winter weather. As to the locks, the best that Nichols could
promise was that the foundation would be complete in the upper
lock and some of the masonry put in place. How much would
depend upon the weather. The lower lock was in bad shape; more
than 20,000 cubic feet of excavation remained to be done. No
masonry work would be undertaken in the lower lock that year, and
the foundation placement would again be determined by the
weather.

Nichols then turned his attention to the coming year and
produced some of the estimates that Harvey should have completed
months before. If all the face stone for the locks was to come from
Malden, in Canada near Detroit, a great shipping effort would be
needed. Here Nichols indicated that he doubted the availability of
prime limestone from Drummond's Island, a doubt that proved to
be only too well founded. All the face stone must be at the Sault by 1
October 1854 to complete the masonry work before frost. Face
stone weighed 4,000 pounds per cubic yard, and 5,000 cubic yards
would be required. This meant that the Canal Company must
import 11,500 tons of limestone. A schooner of 200-ton capacity
needed three weeks for a trip from Detroit and back. In the five
months of shipping time available before 1 October 1854, one
schooner could haul only 1,400 tons of stone. Thus, by Nichols's
simple calculations, the Canal Company would require the services
of eight schooners! Little wonder that after reading Nichols's report
Corning began to press his stockholders.

Transporting backing stone for the lock walls would also present
a problem, according to Nichols. This stone, which need not be of
high quality, could be obtained from several places on Drummond's
Island. However, 23,000 tons would be required, which was more
than the *Dart* could handle in one season. Nor did Nichols make any
allowance for the possibility that the *Dart* might be grounded or
plagued with mechanical problems. Calculating the amount of stone
one mason could set each day, he warned that at least 125 masons
would be needed to complete the job.

There were a few bright spots in Nichols's report. He predicted—
mistakenly, as it turned out—that Harvey would have all the heavy
timber at the Sault by the end of the working season, and that the
Dart could be released for other work. The planking was expected

on contract on 20 September, but would not be needed until the heavy timbers were in place. Nichols reported that Harvey intended to retain 300 men during the winter to work on the excavation. He made only one comment regarding the supervision of the project. "We need a thorough, energetic, and experienced boss mason to take charge of the quarrying, cutting, and laying of the masonry who we should employ at once." Nichols might have added that, if the face stone had to come from Malden, the company would need two such men.[17]

Harvey of course saw a copy of the report and, in a covering series of letters, began to prepare his defense. He stated outright that the excavation and timber work during the 1853 season had been entirely under his direct control. He complained about the difficulties of working 400 miles from his base of supply and explained that it was hard to keep a full work crew on hand because other parties tried to hire the men away from the Canal Company. Nevertheless, and in spite of the cold facts of Nichols's arithmetic, Harvey promised that the masonry would be finished early in the next season. It would seem that, even with some practical experience behind him, Harvey still could not grasp the magnitude of his responsibilities. He concluded to Joy, "I fully concur with Mr. Nichols that it will require extraordinary exertion . . . to open the canal one year from this fall, but I think it *can and will be done*."[18]

Others were not so sure. Canfield reported quietly to Colonel Abert, "The work has not progressed as rapidly during the summer as it should have done in order to assure its completion within the limited time. I think it possible that it may be done—but I am not confident that it will be." Brown also began to doubt that the canal would be completed on time. He began editorial attacks on Harvey, making the obvious criticism that the Canal Company had not employed enough men during the summer. Since he knew more about the rigors of a Sault winter than did Harvey or Nichols, he predicted that very little work would be accomplished after 1 December.[19]

It must have been obvious to the Canal Company directors that Harvey would have to be replaced or at least given a more limited assignment. There had been too many promises leading to too many failures and half-successes. Brooks and Corning set out to find a new superintendent in the late fall of 1853.

Harvey, aware of the move, defended himself to Corning. Heretofore, he had taken great pride in his complete authority at the Sault, and in later years he would again claim this authority with equal pride; but in November 1853 his defenses were completely down. Although noting that Brooks had never indicated any dissatisfaction with work progress, he stated to Corning that he had never expected to do all that was forced upon him and agreed that a new man should be placed in charge of construction.[20]

In his plea to Fairbanks, Harvey expressed more reluctance about his possible replacement. He wrote of his fear that Brooks "may effect some change in my position before I have an average chance to show what I can do." He asked for the opportunity to stay on until 1 June 1854 and then step aside for another man if Brooks was not satisfied with the work accomplished during the winter. Finally, Harvey reminded Fairbanks (who probably did not need to be reminded) that the brothers in St. Johnsbury had championed him when they barely knew him and that his failure would reflect upon them.[21]

However, Brooks was determined on a replacement, and the man he wanted was John T. Clark, an engineer with experience in canal construction. Clark had served as resident engineer, eastern subdivision, middle division of the Erie Canal, and had received a promotion to division engineer. He had served in this post for two years, supervising the enlargement of the canal in his district. He left the canal in 1853 to become chief engineer of the Great Western Railroad. Now, at a directors meeting in Albany on 1 December 1853, he became the Canal Company's choice as a replacement for Harvey. Brooks wrote to him, "We want a smart pushing man to go up to the Sault St. Mary next spring and take charge of the construction of our canal." He offered Clark $5,000 to complete the job. The figure was unusually high, and later Brooks had to defend it to Fairbanks. As it turned out, Clark was not available, and Harvey was given a reprieve.[22]

One promise to the Canal Company Harvey more than fulfilled. He had hoped to retain 300 men at the Sault over the winter, but when the last boat left for Detroit, he found that he had about 400 willing to remain. Some were axemen, who continued to supply timbers for the piers and lock flooring, but most labored in the excavation. No harder work existed in the Sault winter, and the difficulties must at times have seemed insurmountable. When

Harvey ordered that a ditch be dug to the required final depth along one side of the canal for its entire length, the ditch filled with water in a severe rain storm. By the next morning it was solidly packed with ice, and Harvey lost his simple and convenient depth gauge. Often the workers' first job, upon reporting to the excavation site early in the morning, was to locate the tools they had left the day before; time and again these tools would be buried under a deep blanket of snow. The men soon learned to take sightings upon the cranes or other prominent structures before leaving their tools for the night. Harvey reported the frustration that often accompanied the excavation of the final two inches of rock. The men would first have to dig through two feet of ice simply to reach the rock. They then were likely to discover that the final two inches in fact constituted the top part of a granite boulder eighteen inches thick, all of which would have to come out. And yet Harvey advised Fairbanks that the *current working force* would complete the canal, except for the masonry, by 1 August 1854.[23]

During these winter months all hands at the Sault ate breakfast before daylight and went out to work as soon as it was light enough to see. Harvey permitted the men only three-quarters of an hour for dinner at noon; they then worked until dark. Since the winter operation cost the Canal Company $8,000 a month, Harvey insisted on working in all but the most bitter weather. He did permit the men to rest for one-quarter of the day on 2 January, a Monday, when they ate an extra supply of fresh meat and apples in honor of the New Year. Harvey told Fairbanks that the men were so content with this treatment that they voted unanimously to bring the Maine Law (prohibition) to the Sault. He never tried to peddle such nonsense to Brooks or Joy, but he knew that Governor Fairbanks had brought the Maine Law to Vermont.

Thus the year ended with the canal project far behind schedule, assuming it had had a schedule to begin with. Nor could the directors have been much heartened by a fresh attack from Lansing. The auditor general of Michigan wrote denouncing the tax-free status of the grant lands and asking if the reward of 750,000 acres was not sufficiently generous to assure the prompt completion of the canal.[24]

6 Courting Disaster 1854

With Harvey still in control of the canal project, at least for the winter, the work struggled on. Nichols and Glenn stayed at the Sault to give engineering guidance, but Brooks returned to his railroad administration in Detroit, where he was all but cut off from activities at the canal site. Then, without warning, came an unpleasant jolt for everyone connected with the project. On 24 January, Secretary of War Jefferson Davis ordered Captain Canfield to go at once to San Francisco and report for duty to the commanding officer of the Department of the Pacific. To confuse matters even further, one hour later Canfield received a telegram simply stating, "The California order is countermanded. You are retained on the canal."[1]

One would expect that such a telegram would be signed by Davis or even by the president himself, but instead it was signed by Congressman David Stuart of Michigan. It put everyone involved in the project in Michigan in a quandary. Canfield could not accept Stuart's telegram as an order, but he remained in Detroit pending clarification. The Michigan canal commissioners were displeased, and Brooks distressed, at the possibility that a new engineer might insist on drastic changes in the canal design. After waiting in vain for new orders from Washington, Canfield wrote to Stuart asking for clarification and received a second telegram on 16 February: "California order revoked today. D. Stuart." Canfield's father-in-law, Senator Cass, wrote on 17 February confirming the news, but there was still no official order from Davis or Abert.[2] The relief of Canfield could hardly have been Abert's idea. The year before he had urged Congress to increase his staff with additional engineers.

Under an act of Congress passed in 1824 entitled "An Act to procure the necessary Surveys, Plans, and Estimates upon the subject of Roads and Canals," the president was authorized to use army engineers like Canfield on such projects as the Sault Canal. The act, a result of Henry Clay's efforts, gave the president wide discretion as to what constituted works of national importance. Abert, however, complained that he did not have enough men to supervise the projects properly and that Canfield, among others, was overworked. The culprit was probably Jefferson Davis himself. He considered that the practice of using army engineers to direct internal improvement programs was unconstitutional. Such projects, according to Davis, were entirely the responsibility of the states, and the government in Washington must do nothing to help.[3]

Obviously someone had brought considerable pressure on President Pierce to obtain the revoking order, for Pierce was as much an enemy of federal aid to internal improvements as was his secretary of war. The Michigan canal commissioners and Governor Parsons surely asked David Stuart for help. They had told Canfield that they could do nothing with the contractors if he left Michigan, and had even asked him to resign his commission, a suggestion that the captain rejected out of hand. Stuart was in a good position to intervene; the power of army engineers working in cooperation with Congress is well known to students of government. It is even more likely that the Canal Company exerted pressure on Pierce through John E. Thayer of Boston. Pierce had spent the eve of his election to the presidency resting in Thayer's home; by 1854 the president, now a tragic figure, needed the personal support of every friend he had. John Thayer, like his brother Nathaniel, was a major stockholder of both the Michigan Central and the New York Central railroads and thus was in close contact with Forbes and Corning. When the issue was finally settled, Brooks told Fairbanks, "The President took the matter in hand and directed the Secretary to recall [sic] the order."[4]

Finally, on 9 March, Abert sent Canfield his orders to stay in Michigan, along with a copy of the letter from Pierce to Davis. But the secretary of war was not yet through with Canfield. He had delayed, from 16 February to 9 March, in transmitting Pierce's revoking order. Now he ordered Abert to find out why Canfield had not obeyed his original orders immediately. The implication was obvious. Had Canfield obeyed immediately, the Canal Company and Pierce would have been faced with a *fait accompli*. Canfield refrained from asking Abert how he was supposed to *get* to San Francisco in the middle of winter. Instead he threw himself on the mercy of his commander and cited his long record of service and obedience to orders. This was not sufficient, and Canfield was ordered to report to Washington.[5]

In the end Davis had his way in a manner no one had anticipated. Canfield returned to Detroit on Sunday, 16 April, suffering with a cold. The cold worsened on Monday, and by Tuesday morning Canfield was dead. Of him the *Detroit Free Press* wrote:

> He was a most accomplished engineer, with remarkable inventive genius, and great resources in his profession—a gallant soldier, a man of high honor and chivalric feeling, and a warm friend. For firmness and decision of character, and yet extremely modest deportment, he was remarkable. He has left no superior in the service where he passed the most of his life. The loss of such a man can not easily be repaired. It was a public misfortune, as it is a private calamity.[6]

The *Free Press* was correct. It would not be easy to replace Canfield, but Brooks put his mind to it at once. Through January he had continued to ponder over a replacement for Harvey. Since John T. Clark was not available, he settled on William J. McAlpine, a distinguished civil engineer and a veteran of the Erie Canal. Brooks emphasized the importance of obtaining as chief engineer for Michigan a man whose reputation was solidly established in the engineering world. To get a lesser man, he warned, would be to run the risk that such a man might try to build a reputation by making changes in Canfield's plans. Any major change, or several minor ones, would end all chances of completion on time. If McAlpine could not come, Brooks wanted Corning to try once again to get Clark. In the meantime, editor Brown came forth in support of Major Glenn for Canfield's post. By this time Brown's hostility to the canal directors and Harvey was well publicized, and, with Brown as his champion, the Canal Company might have reason to fear Glenn's appointment. For the time being, Governor Parsons made no appointment at all.[7]

At the Sault, Harvey continued to complain about Brooks's treatment of him, and it was obvious that the two men were falling out. Brooks suggested that Harvey had deliberately ignored instructions in 1853, and Harvey resented the criticism. Late in the winter Harvey sent the manager of McKnight's steamship line east to visit Fairbanks and Corning. Ostensibly he was to obtain another bookkeeper, but in his letter of introduction Harvey wrote, "Any information given by him respecting the progress of the canal can be relied upon as impartial and correct." No doubt the information was encouraging.[8]

In spite of assurances from Harvey, however, things continued to go wrong in early 1854. Brooks was unable to give adequate attention to canal matters and sent Corning a list of his February commitments to explain why he could not attend the directors meeting of the Canal Company. He simply could not supervise both the canal project and his railroad. Also in February the subcontracted quarry work fell behind schedule, and Brooks decided in March to cancel the contract. Only half the stone work was completed, and the company would have to take direct charge. Meanwhile, further bad news came down from the Sault. Harvey had anticipated using rock from the excavation for most of the lock backing stone. However, this rock did not prove of sufficient quality to meet the specifications, and the bulk would have to be hauled in from Drummond's Island. Finally, to Brooks's exasperation, Harvey had miscalculated his lumber resources. Either he had underestimated the amount of pine needed, or he had overestimated the resources of the land from which he was taking the trees. In either case, the supply was exhausted when only half the timber for the lower lock was cut. Brooks set off to find a new source of pine near Detroit while Harvey went out on the same mission at the Sault. Brooks insisted that Harvey not be told that they both were looking for pine; he feared that Harvey would stop looking if he heard of the duplication of effort, and he wanted a second supply available at the Sault should his pine be lost at sea on its way north.[9]

Even the weather, which had been so favorable to the project in 1853, turned bad. A storekeeper at the Sault reported that the St. Mary's River was more filled with ice than it had been in sixteen years. This would mean an unusually late date for the opening of navigation. Harvey complained that the weather in March was most severe. He reported that a hurricane struck on 17 March with such ferocity that workmen with their loaded barrows were hurled into the excavation by the force of the wind. The mean temperature recorded at Fort Brady for March 1854 was seven degrees lower than for March 1853. Snow fell on fourteen days, and ice deepened in the excavation. Still, Harvey was enthusiastic, claiming excellent progress and an ultimate cost that would be below estimate.[10]

Fairbanks by no means shared Harvey's confidence. He now had more time to think about the affairs of the Canal Company, since the voters of Vermont had retired him from public office after one year as governor. Apparently the people of Vermont were not as enthusiastic over the Maine Law that Fairbanks had signed as was their governor. Fairbanks wrote to Corning that his "solicitude was not so much in view of anything left or liable to be left undone . . . as in view of the disastrous consequences of failure." There was no question in his mind as to where the fault lay. He deeply regretted the failure of the Canal Company to appoint a competent superintendent in the previous year; Harvey obviously could not handle the job. Fairbanks then made several suggestions to Corning that ultimately saved the company. The Canal Company must secure the undivided services of John Brooks for at least three months after the opening of navigation; another man must be given the sole responsibility for the procurement of a proper labor force; and the entire supervisory structure must be put in order. Fairbanks concluded by expressing the hope that from now on all the directors would pay more attention to the project and make a personal inspection at the Sault at the earliest date. Corning sent the letter on to Brooks after adding the words, "I beg to say that I fully concur." Brooks, however, immediately protested that he could not leave the affairs of the railroad.[11]

Before the directors could meet in May, they received another discouraging report from Nichols. Excavation was proceeding too slowly along the entire length of the canal, and six feet of ice in the lock pits prevented workmen from putting the timbers in place. Nevertheless, Nichols hoped to have the ice removed in ten days. He also acknowledged Brooks's order to construct a second dock at the lower end of the canal so that the work would not be held up for lack of docking space when the great shipping effort began. Finally Nichols reported that work had begun on the cofferdam in Lake Superior. Two heavy sea walls of rock had been carted out on the ice to form a 450-foot enclosure. As soon as the ice melted, this rock would serve as the foundation of the dam.[12]

If this sounded like a peculiar way to build a cofferdam, Brooks apparently was unaware of it. He was more concerned with the fact that Harvey, as usual, had failed to plan ahead. In this case the problem was the location of the second dock. Harvey had pushed it out into the St. Mary's River in a direct line with the canal, where it would have prevented the work of underwater excavation until all the stone had been landed. Brooks notified Fairbanks that he had been forced to overrule Harvey by ordering the dock moved farther north, although the change involved an additional week of work. He wrote, "It will not due [sic] to let any part of the work get in the way of any other part." He also promised to try to arrange his railroad affairs so that he could give more attention to the canal.[13]

In early May the directors of the Canal Company finally took the necessary steps to reorganize the project. It was agreed that Brooks should go to the Sault and take direct charge of the entire operation for the summer. No doubt Forbes did not relish the idea of losing his superintendent for that period, but he would have liked even less the idea of watching the value of his Canal Company stock drop to zero. Director John Seymour agreed to take on the responsibility of finding a suitable labor force and getting it to the Sault, for which the directors agreed to pay him $3,000 and expenses. Harvey could keep his title as general agent, but he would carry out only the chores Brooks thought him capable of performing without wrecking the company. George S. Frost had been appointed a canal land agent by Governor Parsons in June 1853, and the directors now gave him full responsibility for all land claims in 1854. Finally, directors Fairbanks and Seymour agreed to visit the project in June. Except for Brooks, they were the first directors to make a personal inspection.[14]

John Woods Brooks would bear the ultimate responsibility; after May 1854 the success or failure of the canal project rested squarely on his shoulders. He was still a relatively young man and would celebrate (if he had time) his thirty-fifth birthday at the Sault on 2 August. He was a native of Stow, Massachusetts, and had received an academy education and then studied engineering under Loammi Baldwin, the father of civil engineering in the United States. At the age of twenty, Brooks became the chief engineer for the Boston and Maine Railroad. Later, as superintendent of the Auburn and Rochester Railroad, he made the acquaintance of Corning. In 1846 he joined Joy and Corning in persuading Forbes and others to buy the

Michigan Central Railroad from the state of Michigan. He then served as superintendent of the Michigan Central from 1846 to 1855.[15]

While Brooks waited impatiently for the opening of navigation to the Sault, he received a bit of news that would have encouraged him had he not been acquainted with Harvey's habits of exaggeration. According to the agent, all the timber needed for the locks was now at hand. Harvey admitted that he had helped himself to Canadian timber, since he had exhausted all the nearby sources of pine. Unfortunately Harvey's "at hand" did not mean at the Sault, as Fairbanks later noted.[16]

The navigation season finally opened when the ice cleared out of the St. Mary's River in the second week of May. Brooks notified Corning that he would go to the Sault on 15 May. Corning's partner Gilbert Davidson planned to accompany him in order to make a firsthand report in Albany and to see if the project needed anything that the Corning enterprises could furnish. Joy, meanwhile, wanted Brooks to go to Chicago on railroad business, and Brooks had to tell his friend what life would be like for the next few months. Before boarding his ship in Detroit, he wired, "I can not go to Chicago any way. Sault uses me up completely." He also urged Corning to call a directors meeting at the Sault at the earliest possible date.[17]

There would be no directors meeting at the Sault that year, but Fairbanks and Seymour arrived during the first week in June. They were just in time to watch the first of the great timbers for the lower lock foundation set in place. Each longitudinal timber was one foot square and rested one foot from its neighbor. None ran the full length of the lock, 350 feet, since pine does not grow to that height; but each was as long as nature provided. Once the longitudinal timbers were in place, the carpenters bolted them to solid rock. On top of these timbers went the transverse beams, also one foot square with one-foot gaps between. Workmen bolted the transverse beams to the rock and filled the intervening spaces with well-packed sand and gravel. Carpenters would next spike the regular lock flooring, three-inch-thick pine, to the beams. Only then could the masons set to work on the walls. Brooks estimated that less than one-fifteenth of the oak timber was at hand, and oak timber must be used directly under the sidewalls.[18]

Fairbanks considered the situation critical. In his report to

Corning, he stated that the project fell short of expectations in all respects and cited an example of the many frustrations that beset Brooks. In spite of the promise from Harvey that all the timber was at hand, 4,000 badly needed feet were still resting, as late as 6 June, on land near Hay Lake, waiting for the *Dart*. The two bargeloads of timber being shipped from Detroit were also long overdue. The steamer escorting the barges had foundered in the lake, and the *Dart* had gone to the rescue. Brooks, Seymour, and Fairbanks decided to purchase another tug for the company. As soon as the timber was really at hand, the *Dart* and her sister ship would be needed to tow the schooners with the face stone up the St. Mary's River, a distance of sixty miles.[19]

Brooks estimated that the floor of the lower lock would be completed by 9 June. Fairbanks wrote that he would be pleased if it were completed by 15 June, but on 17 June the carpenters were still waiting for the heavy timbers to arrive to complete the foundation. The failure to have timber cut and on hand was inexcusable. Just as serious was the fact that none of the backing stone had arrived from Drummond's Island and none of the face stone from Malden. Worse yet, for the first time the ominous word "cholera" was used as Fairbanks told Corning that isolated cases had been reported near the company quarry. To date none of the company's men had contracted the disease, but Fairbanks warned Corning of what might happen should this killer appear at the Sault. As to the rest of the project, none of the difficult underwater excavation had been done, and above water Nichols estimated that 35,000 cubic yards remained to be hauled out of the ditch. Once the lock floors were completed, the carpenters could use the rest of the summer to build the upper docks and the caisson gate. Fairbanks completed his pessimistic report and signed it. Then he reopened the letter to add that the missing *Dart* and her two barges had just been located, aground, on a mud flat twenty-five miles below. "We must have two more tugs—not just one," he concluded.[20]

By the end of June, the usually optimistic Cleveland *Daily Plain Dealer* began to doubt that the project would be completed that year. It recorded that only a fraction of the required stone had arrived from Malden, and it blamed the company's troubles on the workers, who were "a little worse than beasts of the field—they guzzle down the meanest kind of poison whisky in quantities.

Several . . . working on the canal have fallen victim to intemperate and filthy habits and a complete recklessness of diet." The *Plain Dealer* refrained from pointing out that there was little else for the men to do. In 1854 there was not even a completed church at the Sault, but grog shops abounded.[21]

On 15 July, Brooks sent out a major warning. "With our present force we can not finish the canal this year." Seymour's efforts to find men must be reinforced. Brooks ordered Joy to find a person qualified to recruit at least forty men along the line of any railroad, or in Chicago. The pay would still be $1 per day and board, with the company paying the fare to the Sault. Brooks also called for fifteen more masons plus a foreman. He concluded, "They are needed *now* and not ten days hence if it is possible to get them here in 8 [underscored twice by Brooks] days." With this message began a frantic scramble for labor that lasted into the fall of 1854.[22]

At the outset Brooks could not "borrow" construction workers from the Michigan Central Railroad, since the road did not have a construction crew in its employ. Railroad building was sporadic in nature, and the roads usually relied on specialized construction companies to do their building. The Canal Company would be forced to find its own men, and Joy was not the only one to help. Brooks also called upon the Michigan Central's agents in Detroit, Buffalo, and New York, Seymour in Utica, and a Mr. Clark in Albany. He sent a special messenger to bring eighty men from Montreal, and he asked Fairbanks to find from fifty to seventy good laborers in Vermont. He warned all concerned that it would not do to send men unescorted to the Sault. From his experience he knew that Upper Peninsula mineowners would approach such men on the boats from Detroit and hire half of them.[23]

Seymour did his job well. He entered into agreement with the New York agent of the Michigan Central to transport the men on the railroad's steamboats from Buffalo to Detroit, where Whitwood would take charge. The Michigan Central would receive $1 per man transported and 20¢ per meal served. By 4 August, Seymour had paid out over $1,000 of Canal Company funds for transportation of labor to the Sault. On the day before Brooks had announced that he now had a sufficient work force and that the project was advancing as well as could be expected.[24]

Brooks had no idea that disaster was heading to the Sault along with its new labor force. In light of today's medical knowledge, it is not surprising that cholera struck at the project. It would have been a miracle if it had not. In 1854, however, it was assumed that the disease was the end product of sinful or vicious living, a judgment of God. The relationship between vice, poverty, and cholera was firmly established.[25]

The warning signs were everywhere in 1854 at the Sault, but no one could—or would—read them. The area around the shanties was filthy; men working eleven and a half hours a day had little energy or inclination to spend much time in housekeeping chores. Fairbanks had noted the presence of cholera near the company's quarries in June, and in the same month George Porter notified his partner, "Cholera is rife in this land." "This land" was Detroit, and the bulk of the labor force had to pass through it on the way to the canal. Both the *Detroit Free Press* and the Cleveland *Daily Plain Dealer* emphatically denied that cholera had reached the Sault. The *Plain Dealer* attributed the few deaths that had occurred among the workingmen to intemperate habits. In July, Brown claimed that the health at the Sault was never better, with no illness in the village and little in the work camp. On 29 July he published a statement signed by two Sault doctors and a three-man board of health to the effect that rumors of cholera at the Sault were false.[26]

The disease struck hard in August. Journalist Brown reported the first case on 5 August, making the standard statement that the stricken man was a "miserable drunkard" to begin with and noting that he had recovered. For almost a month no more was said. Other than the various ship captains, who would certainly be reluctant to mention the disease, Brown was the only voice of influence speaking from the Sault. If he had published the full extent of the ravages of cholera at the canal site, he would have seriously, perhaps fatally, injured the Canal Company's efforts to replace the sick and dead men with fresh workers. Moreover such news would destroy the image of the Sault as a cholera-free health retreat. Brown elected to remain silent through the critical period. He published a "cure" for cholera in September without indicating the present need for the treatment recommended. When Harvey jumped into local politics in October, Brown advised him to spend more time keeping his own

votes alive, without hinting as to what was wrong with the voters.
Finally, in October, he reported the total number of deaths at the
Sault for the last fourteen months without listing any of the causes.
Eight strangers passing through the village, twelve citizens of the
Sault, and eighty-eight canal workers had died. Brown claimed that
many of the latter would have died anyway, because of their
"reckless habits."[27]

As Brooks knew, far more than eighty-eight of his men were dead,
and still more were too sick to work. H. D. Ward, supervisor of
construction and second only to Brooks, died of cholera. C. E.
Bigelow, the company's chief clerk, took his family back home to
Connecticut because of bad health. Brooks told Joy that panic had
swept through the ranks of the workers, and for a time he could keep
only half the men at their tasks. Of his entire force of 1,700 men, over
one-tenth died, and there were no estimates of the number who
recovered but were too weak to work. Even the weather favored the
disease. The mean temperature for the month of September was
eight degrees higher than the year before. A high of ninety-eight was
recorded for the month at Fort Brady. Rain fell on sixteen days. It
was fortunate for the company that Brooks did not succumb. He
wrote, "I keep on my feet the whole day, every day and a twelve hour
walk per day is what I am not used to, and although the stock I hold
in this enterprise is worth . . . $40,000 I have many times
regretting [sic] going into it." To add to Brooks's problems, part of
the labor force staged a riot on the nights of 20-21 August. A number
of men were arrested, and one was so violent that he had to be
lodged in the Fort Brady guardhouse. The real culprits were
ignorance and poor camp sanitation. In contrast, the health of the
soldiers at Fort Brady remained normal through the entire year.[28]

The cholera epidemic spurred new recruiting efforts to replace the
sick and dead men. From Albany alone 472 men left for the Sault
between 7 September and 30 September 1854. Seymour employed
"laborlookers" to find men, just as Brooks and Frost had hired
landlookers to explore for possible grant lands. The story of Joseph
Knoblock was typical, at least up to a point. Seymour employed him
in August to look for canal labor. His first trip took him through
Syracuse, Rochester, and Buffalo, and by the time he reached
Detroit he had picked up 33 men. Whitwood took charge of the men
at Detroit, and Knoblock returned to Utica for more employees.

After three days there, he stopped in Oneida, Rochester, and Buffalo, and returned again to Detroit, this time with 35 workers. It was the last trip that Knoblock ever made. He died in Detroit on 2 October, after working for the Canal Company less than two months. In December a friend of his widow asked Seymour for payment of Knoblock's last expenses; the amount was $44.94, including the cost of his burial in Detroit. During the next four months Seymour made several small payments, the sum of which was approximately the amount claimed less the burial cost. A man could die in the service of the Canal Company, but he was buried on his own time.[29]

Brooks described the workers as they arrived at the Sault. "They are sick, starved, lean, lank, slim, light of build, fallow, about half of them will weigh under 100 lbs. They look as if they had come from abroad or an emigrant [sic] ship lately." He told Seymour that he wanted no more such recruits. In Detroit, Whitwood too began to doubt the value of the emergency drive for workers. He wrote to Seymour, "The men hired in N.Y. are generly to [sic] weak and small for such heavy work." However, "as the cry is for men! men! you had better continue to forward more." Seymour, faced with conflicting requests, decided to continue the search.[30]

In spite of cholera and the weather, Brooks pushed on with the construction. An observer described him as being a perfect Napoleon in the way he worked his men. The comparison was appropriate enough, since Forbes wrote that Brooks was having more difficulty that summer than Lord Raglan was experiencing in the Crimea. Brooks warned Joy that he must remain at the Sault for the rest of the season, unless the directors decided not to finish in contract time. The completion date of the work became a source of much conjecture, with the *Daily Plain Dealer* making the most pessimistic prediction. Estimating the date as August 1855, the *Plain Dealer* remarked, "The ship canal is a big work for so small a one."[31]

By 22 July, Brooks could report that though the masonry in the upper lock was more than half finished, it had barely been started in the lower. He anticipated that the cofferdam would be completed at Lake Superior in three more days; he intended to use a horse-powered punch to break up the underwater rock. At the lower end of the canal, a temporary cofferdam was in place, with a steam pump at work. As soon as the south pier was no longer needed for unloading stone, the dam would be extended for the final excavation. Brooks sent Fairbanks a sketch of his work at this end of the canal. At the same time Brown warned all concerned in the Upper Peninsula to be sure to lay in their winter supplies early. Because of canal needs, there would be great pressure on transportation facilities of all kinds.[32]

Meanwhile, there was good news from Lansing. After a lapse of several months, Canfield's position as chief engineer for the State of Michigan was filled when, in early July, Governor Parsons appointed John T. Clark, Brooks's original choice for the job. The Canal Company officers thus attained another goal, although Major Glenn retained his original post as assistant state engineer. It remained to be seen if Clark would be as cooperative as Brooks had hoped.[33]

In Detroit, Whitwood was confident of success. He had reported on 28 September that the last of the face stone had left Malden. Brooks hoped to have the masonry completed by the middle of October, and Whitwood promised that the last of the timber for the gates would leave for the Sault on 29 September. The Canal Company was lucky that Whitwood, who was responsible for the forwarding of the men and supplies in 1854, had remained in good health. He wrote, "Fortunately I am well while many choice spirits connected with the Canal Company have gone to their long home."[34]

During the fall some of the directors decided to see for themselves how the canal progressed, and on 11 October, Fairbanks, Corning, and Seymour arrived at the Sault on an inspection trip. It was Corning's first and only visit during construction. The result of this inspection was a letter written to reassure the stockholders.

Its authors could report that the masonry work in the locks had been completed except for the top coping stone. The cofferdams were both secure, and the underwater excavation could begin. The directors stated that they were sure the entire project would be completed by contract time next May. In order that the stockholders might appreciate the magnitude of the undertaking, the writers noted that "the combined length of both sides of the locks is considerably more than one-quarter of a mile of solid faced masonry and ten feet thick at the base all of which is laid in hydrolic [sic] cement and in the quality of its stone and style of finish is not inferior to any in the State of New York."[35]

It was a carefully worded letter giving no hint of mismanagement. The directors praised both Brooks and Harvey, even though they blamed the latter in private for their troubles. In spite of their description to the stockholders, they clearly failed to grasp the magnitude of the project; a look at the drawings and specifications and a little simple arithmetic would have improved their judgment. Finally, the report made no mention of the progress at the upper caisson gate.

As the stockholders contemplated the report, its inaccuracies were already becoming sadly apparent at the Sault. Two weeks after the directors had declared the cofferdams to be secured, Harvey reported that the Lake Superior dam had collapsed for the third time. "Words had better not express my chagrin," he wrote. Anticipating future developments, he added that no amount of money could tempt him into staying a second winter, although if the directors should require it, he would not be at liberty to refuse. Brooks meanwhile ordered the bulk of his labor force to the Superior end of the canal to rebuild the cofferdam and start underwater excavation.[36]

It seemed to Brooks that everything conspired against him in November. On the first day of the month, many of the men refused to report to work and instead paraded the streets of Sault Ste. Marie, carrying banners in honor of All Saints Day. The parade soon deteriorated into another labor strike. Rumors circulated that wages would now be reduced from $26 to $20 per month. The men had not been paid in October, and another rumor circulated that the Canal Company did not intend to pay until spring, so as to keep the workers on the job all winter. Brown encouraged the rumors by printing them. The strike lasted three days before Brooks could get his full force back to work—and then the storms came.[37]

Brooks had two hopes in mid-November. He wanted Clark and the canal commissioners to visit the project that fall and make a statement strong enough to persuade Michigan to release the grant lands. He also hoped for twelve to sixteen more construction days, enough to allow him to put a ship through the canal. Neither hope was realized. Clark refused to go north, and Brooks did not get the time he needed. Snow fell on fourteen days in November, and a low of one degree above zero was recorded at Fort Brady. This time the upper cofferdam held, but so violent were the storms that water rushed over the top. High waves swamped the horse dredge at the lower end of the project, with the loss of three horses. It took Brooks's men three days to raise the dredge. Fairbanks wrote, "I learned that poor Harvey is to remain at the Sault another winter. It must be a sad disappointment to him and Mr. Brooks that Mr. Clark and the Commission failed to go up."[38]

The directors had a further reason for wanting the lands granted to them in 1854. A major change in political fortunes was in the making. The year before, Vermont voters had retired Fairbanks from public office for signing a Maine Law. Now, in 1854, the people of New York voted Horatio Seymour out of office for vetoing one. As a result, John Seymour would no longer be the brother of the governor of New York. Meanwhile, as the Canal Company was losing ground politically, its old enemies were gaining—for reasons that had nothing to do with the canal. While Brooks was struggling at the Sault in July, a political convention met in Jackson, Michigan. Here Michigan Whigs, Free Soilers, and Democrats disgusted with the Pierce administration united to form the Republican party. Canal Company enemy Jacob Howard emerged from the convention a leader. He became the Republican candidate for attorney general of Michigan, and in November the entire Republican slate swept to victory. The result was that the Canal Company would face a hostile attorney general and an unknown governor, Kinsley S. Bingham, in 1855. The only sure friend the company would have in office would be United States Secretary of the Interior Robert McClelland.[39]

Clark and the commission ignored all pressure to visit the project in 1854. Brooks had warned Joy earlier in the year that the commission had decided not to endorse the canal until it could see how the project withstood the winter of 1854–55. The decision was reasonable, and the commissioners refused to reverse it. While the directors worried over the commission, time ran out on Brooks. Navigation closed down much earlier than usual, and by 1 December the bulk of the work force was back in Detroit and paid off for the last time. Seymour had sent the last payroll, $54,875, to the Sault in two ships to halve the risk of loss. Harvey remained on the project with about one hundred men, while Seymour wrote, "If Clark had gone up I would have been satisfied."[40]

Perhaps the most satisfied man on the ship coming down from the Sault was Charles W. Chapel, who had just been elected to the

Michigan legislature. His excavation was completed to the one percent that Harvey could handle within the next four months. In his pocket he carried a gold watch and chain presented to him by Brooks. The watch was inscribed:

St. M. F. S. C. C.

to

C. W. CHAPEL

FIDELITY AND ENERGY

With this fine timepiece Chapel would have no excuse for being late for legislative roll calls, some of which might involve the affairs of the Canal Company. Brooks himself carried with him a less felicitous token of the arduous summer. He spent Christmas in Boston, sick in bed, under the eye of John Murray Forbes. Many days passed before he was well enough to travel again.[41]

7 The Treacherous Editor

The relationship between Harvey and J. Venen Brown played a major role in the affairs of the Canal Company during the construction years. Harvey had trusted Brown, putting him on the company payroll to give favorable publicity and making him a canal land agent. After Harvey's arrival at the Sault in 1853, Brown entered no more claims as the agent of the company, but he supervised the work of the landlookers and turned the results over to Harvey for filing. As late as September 1853, Harvey expressed confidence in Brown's general oversight at the Sault land office. During the summer Brown's newspaper carried glowing accounts of the canal's progress and of its general agent. The editor called Harvey "indefatigable" and praised the engineering achievements of Captain Canfield. Brown's eastern exchanges could reprint these reports, and his support would therefore be helpful if the company were to float a bond issue. However, the amicable relationship was soon to change.[1]

A dispute between Brown and Harvey began in October 1853. It worsened during the following winter, and by the spring of 1854 Brown had become hostile to the Canal Company and its general agent. The disagreement arose over the ownership of the limestone quarry on Drummond's Island, where Harvey expected to get most of the facing rock for the canal locks. Although the quarry was registered in the Sault land office as the property of Brown, Harvey considered that it belonged to the Canal Company. When the two men visited the quarry in October 1853, Brown demanded $5,000 from the Canal Company for the right to extract stone. Harvey, on the other hand, insisted that the company already had the right, since Brown, as company agent, should have claimed the land for the company and not for himself. Harvey proposed instead that the company give Brown all the improvements made on the site, including the dock, as soon as the canal project was completed. He estimated the value of these improvements to be $2,000.[2]

When the two men could not reach an agreement, Harvey sailed for Detroit to obtain help from Brooks. Once again Brooks had to abandon his railroad duties to attend to canal business. In November 1853 he returned to the Sault with Harvey to conclude a deal with Brown. The Sault editor would permit the company to extract as much limestone as it needed at a price to be set by a committee of three. Brown and Brooks would each select one member of this committee, and the two selected would try to agree on a third.[3]

This agreement was defeated before it had a chance to go into effect. Upon his arrival at the Sault, Brooks conferred with Harvey as to the nature of the land on Drummond's Island, especially the two lots giving access to the quarry. The two men then called upon Ebenezer Warner at the Sault land office to obtain the exact description of the access land, after which they undertook to prepare papers to claim and purchase the lots outright. But they had not worked fast enough. On the day before the Brooks-Brown agreement was to be signed, Brown had purchased the access land for himself. At the time he was still in the employ of the Canal Company and was supposedly looking after its interests. The lots, both in Township 42N, Range 6E, together with the lots Brown had claimed for himself in May, effectively sealed off the quarry from the St. Mary's River. This was more than enough for Harvey and Brooks. They terminated Brown's association with the Canal Company before the end of November.[4]

It was fortunate for the company that Brooks had discovered another source of high-quality limestone earlier in the year near Malden, Canada West, across the river from Detroit. Now, however, the company would be forced to ship tons of stone a distance of over 300 miles, whereas Drummond's Island was only 35 miles from the Sault. Harvey's reckless judgment and Brown's greed had cost the company dearly. The company also had acquired an unscrupulous enemy at the Sault.

The 2 January 1854 issue of the *Lake Superior Journal* was the last one in which Brown listed himself as land agent for the Canal Company in the Upper Peninsula. Although anxious to attack Harvey and the administration of the company, the Sault editor was handicapped because his journal appeared but once a month during the winter. In the meantime Harvey prepared for a rumor campaign should Brown choose to launch one in Lansing. He wrote to Deodatus Whitwood that he had a letter from Brown dated 18 January 1854 demanding $8,000 blackmail as his price for refraining from a paper war against the Canal Company. Since Harvey's own letter to Whitwood was dated 4 January 1854, the Brown letter could have existed only in Harvey's fertile imagination. Brown in any case was too clever to have written such a letter; nevertheless, Whitwood was free to spread the story around Lansing as a weapon against him.[5]

Harvey's action had been unscrupulous; Brown's attack was no less so. In his first charge he accused Harvey of manslaughter. When the last boat sailed for Detroit in the late fall of 1853, three men had been left behind, lost in the woods on Drummond's Island. Two of these men survived by living on acorns, but the third died. Brown claimed that, having failed to look for the men, Harvey was to blame. Further, Harvey had sent a work party of fifty men to Drummond's Island in the middle of the winter. They had crossed the ice with scant provisions, anticipating relief from the *Dart*. Now they were in a precarious position because of the late opening of the navigation season, and Harvey was doing nothing to save them. "How often are we to have such inhumanity exhibited among us?" Brown demanded, well aware that sometimes eastern newspapers reprinted his Sault reports and that the Canal Company directors received the *Lake Superior Journal*. His attempt to make the company repugnant in the eyes of the general public and undermine whatever confidence the directors still had in Harvey failed, however, and no one paid any attention to the manslaughter charge.[6]

Having exhausted this charge, Brown turned to an accusation of theft. In May 1854 he notified the prosecuting attorney of Chippewa County that Harvey had trespassed on the school section of Township 46N, Range 2E, near Hay Lake (now Lake Nicolet). From this section Harvey had removed timber in the value of untold thousands, thus robbing generations of little children. Brown rejected Harvey's contention that he had bought the land from Governor Parsons. He also notified the state authorities of Harvey's guilt and published the story in his newspaper.[7]

The governor could not ignore such a serious charge. Because of the unusual circumstances existing at the time of Michigan's admission to the union, Congress had given Michigan governors more responsibility for the school lands than most governors possessed. Parsons therefore sent Judge Amos Gould of Shiawassee to the Sault to investigate. The judge soon discovered that Brown's charges were correct. The magnificent stand of pine that Harvey had located a year before, when he decided not to subcontract for heavy timber, stood on Section 16 of the township in question. Brown had been quite aware of this for almost a year, since, as land agent for the Canal Company, he had tried to buy the property from Ebenezer Warner in 1853, only to discover that Warner could not sell school land. Upon arrival at the Sault, Judge Gould observed a quantity of pine that had been taken from the school land, and he charged Harvey with theft. The latter admitted to everything but pleaded the urgency of the canal project and its importance as a public work. Not only was the timber essential for the canal, but it was also easily accessible and therefore less costly than timber extracted from farther inland. Harvey must have been persuasive, for the judge decided that the Canal Company could keep the timber upon payment of $1,000 damages and $200 expenses. When paid this amount, Gould notified the prosecuting attorney that the state was satisfied, and Harvey continued to extract timber from the school land.[8]

In the following year, however, a select committee of the Michigan State Senate investigated this strange transaction. It heard testimony from Brown, Gould, and Samuel Whitney, who was a witness to the timber theft. After deliberation the committee decided "that the Company despoiled this section of its present value by cutting off timber because it was believed they could get it in this manner cheaper than they could elsewhere get it." The committee estimated the value of the timber to be $5 per acre and proposed to exonerate the company if it would agree to buy the section at $4 per acre. (The company had already tried to buy the land, in 1853, and had assumed in good faith that Gould had the authority to complete the deal in 1854.) The state senators seemed to be more interested in embarrassing Governor Parsons than in making trouble for the Canal Company, and they denounced his handling of the situation. They also noted, however, that Harvey's arrangement with Gould had created animosity toward the Canal Company in parts of the state. Brown's newspaper campaign was succeeding.[9]

In venting his wrath at Harvey, Brown forgot that he might bring himself down further than his target. On the day he denounced the timber theft, he took a step toward ending his own career at the Sault. In an effort to further undermine the canal, he urged press and business interests in Chicago to lobby for a railroad with a southern terminal in Chicago and a northern terminal in Marquette, Michigan, on the shore of Lake Superior. Such a railroad would bypass the Sault canal and give to Chicago the trade of the Upper Peninsula. Brown wrote, "The completion of the Sault Ste. Marie canal will, by a natural law of commerce tend to deepen the current trade in channels already alluded to [Cleveland and Detroit], unless *force* is applied to divert it into other channels—perhaps even to create other—and Chicago has that force." Nevertheless, in the same issue of the *Lake Superior Journal* most of the advertising space had been purchased by the merchants and businessmen of Cleveland and Detroit. In fact, the Chicago plan was nothing but a pipe dream. The Chicago and Northwestern Railroad would not be able to push a line into the Upper Peninsula until 1872, and even this would be faint competition for the canal.[10]

It is not surprising that when Fairbanks visited the Sault in June 1854, he had another purpose besides inspecting the canal's progress. The Canal Company directors had decided that Brown's editorial assaults could no longer go unanswered. On 27 May, Brown had reported that the company was using soft sandstone instead of limestone for the lock facing, which, he said, "will be likely to last about as long as they will be in making the wall." He also condemned the Malden limestone, saying it would crack at the first frost—a questionable claim, since at that time the limestone had not even arrived at the Sault for Brown to examine. Brown called the owners of the company "foreign capitalists" who never came near to observe the progress of the work, but on the day he published this accusation, three directors were at the Sault.[11]

Some of Brown's criticisms were justified, however. He pointed out that the movement of stone was too slow because the company would not pay for prompt freighting. While noting that the actual building of the locks was the most difficult, expensive, and tedious part of the whole undertaking, he also observed that as yet no underwater work had started at either end of the canal. Coffer dams would be required, and these would not be easy to put up or to maintain. But the greatest error of all, Brown claimed, lay in trusting Harvey, who had no experience in canal construction and whose operations were often penny wise and pound foolish. In response to an article in the *Detroit Inquirer*, Brown retorted, "The prospect of the completion of this canal is much stronger, we presume, with those who found their opinion on the report of the Agent or interested persons, than with those familiar with the management and progress of the work." As a rule the *Inquirer* had published optimistic reports about the project, but now it pointed out that "financial arrangements were not being well digested." Brown held that "improper digestion" applied to all phases of the project, and declared that the Canal Company would have absolutely no grounds on which to apply for an extension of time from the Michigan government.[12]

These attacks frequently had the desired effect, and Fairbanks could not afford to ignore them. As early as April 1854, Samuel Churchill in New York City warned Pruyn that the canal stockholders of the city were upset and beginning to ask questions about the management of the company. Churchill, who was one of the New York incorporators of the Canal Company, enclosed a clipping from the *Journal of Commerce*, about the Malden face stone cracking in the frost. He suggested that a public statement might be made by one of the canal officers to calm the stockholders, and in June, Fairbanks prepared such a statement and had it published over his and Chapel's signatures in the Detroit *Tribune*.[13]

It must have pleased Fairbanks when the *Detroit Free Press* picked up his report and published a highly favorable account of the canal's progress. The paper gave Harvey and Chapel much credit for their energetic efforts, noting that Brooks, Fairbanks, and Seymour had just examined the books, vouchers, and general progress and had "expressed their unqualified approbation of the whole, as creditable to the integrity, energy, and fidelity of the agent, and the

skill and faithfulness of the engineers and overseers of the work."
Finally, the *Free Press* reported that three-fourths of the stone had
been quarried and dressed and that full credit for this accomplishment should be attributed to the skill and energy of Brooks.[14]

On 1 July, Brown lashed back at the Canal Company. In his
editorial he claimed that he had reprinted the entire Fairbanks-
Chapel statement as published in the Detroit *Tribune*, though
actually he had not done so. Brown charged that Fairbanks was
using his reputation as former governor of Vermont to cover up for
the miserable failure of the company. He called the description of
the Malden face stone by Fairbanks and Chapel a lie and continued
to insist that the stone was completely unsuitable for the Sault
climate. Fairbanks had claimed that the contractors and the general
public had no idea of the difficulties to be encountered while
working at the Sault; Brown responded that it was not to the
contractors' credit that they had rushed willingly into a job they
knew nothing about. This was true enough. Brown lied, however,
when he insisted that the difficulties had been well known in the
area before the contract was signed. In fact, both he and his
predecessor, John Ingersoll, had understated the potential problems
because they wanted the work done as soon as possible and were
reluctant to scare away potential builders. Responding to what he
called a charge of blackmail in the Fairbanks-Chapel letter, Brown
jeered that the Canal Company was in no position to pay blackmail
to anyone. It had already paid the Michigan legislature, first for the
original canal bill and then for the supplementary legislation placing
the grant lands on a tax-free basis for five years. Moreover, the
company had paid off the canal commission for the contract. Brown
suggested that what funds remained must be carefully preserved to
bribe a future legislature for an extension of time. Thus there would
be no money left to pay off Brown. Finally, Brown repeated the
entire story of the theft of lumber from the little schoolchildren, a
story that Fairbanks and Chapel had found it convenient to
ignore.[15]

As the paper war went on, Brown held two advantages; he was the
only reporter at the Sault, and from time to time there was truth in
his allegations. He only weakened his case when he indulged in gross
exaggeration, as in the matter of the bribery charges. The company's
major advantage lay in the reputation of its officers, especially

Fairbanks in the Midwest and Corning in the East. If the canal could be completed on time and to specification, the Canal Company would have the ultimate answer to Brown.

Sometime in the summer of 1854, Harvey decided to dabble in Upper Peninsula politics, a decision Brown was not long in discovering. Brown declared that the Canal Company intended to enter candidates for all the legislative positions in the Upper Peninsula and that Harvey, with his control over the horde of canal workers, would dominate. "They will do as they did to the last legislature, resort to every species of bribery and corruption to carry their ends," he predicted. To strengthen his case, Brown described a new fraud being perpetrated on the people of Michigan. He stated that in 1853 Harvey and other agents had claimed far more than the 750,000 acres to which the company was entitled and had filed these claims in the various land offices in Michigan. Now that the company had had time for a thorough examination of the land, it was rejecting the least valuable acres. Brown claimed that he had opposed this fraud in 1853 and had lost his job as land agent in reprisal. He did not explain why he had waited eight months to make this revelation.[16]

There was some truth in the charge that the Canal Company had overclaimed its allotment. George Frost, who assumed responsibility for all claims, ruled off about 10,000 acres in the Upper Peninsula when he filed his list with the secretary of interior. The total claim in the Upper Peninsula was 252,958.10 acres, so the claim deducted did not constitute a significant fraction. However, the bulk of the deleted claims, 6,440 acres in Delta County, hardly represented the most valuable of the lands. Brown could charge fraud, but there were at least two other possibilities. In a time and place of poor communications, with several men filing claims at the Lower Peninsula's three land offices and Harvey filing at the Sault, no one knew precisely when to stop. In addition, Harvey and the others may have been careless.[17]

The new charges did not seem to bother Harvey, who on 6 September went to Eagle River, Michigan, for business and political reasons. He wanted to construct a road from Copper Harbor to a location on the Ontonagon River, so that copper could be hauled out of the district. At Eagle River he formed a resolutions committee to petition the legislature for aid. He also attended the Democratic caucus that selected the candidate for representative from Houghton County. If Harvey had the influence that Brown attributed to him, he did not use it on 6 September. The Eagle River men nominated Canal Company enemy Abner Sherman by a unanimous vote.[18]

Brown was not pleased with Harvey's political adventures, nevertheless, and he anticipated trouble at the Sault Democratic nominating caucus. He wrote, "One might suppose that the Co. could find enough for their agent to do near or on the work, especially one of such uniform kindness in taking care of the sick and dying. The cause of humanity, and perhaps that of the Co. would be served in kindly endeavoring to keep their voters alive till after the convention." Brown feared that hundreds of canal workers would pack the Sault caucus, and he must have been embarrassed at what actually happened. The Sault Democratic caucus nominated Charles W. Chapel, the superintendent of canal excavation. However, there were only twenty-two votes cast, with Chapel receiving twenty. It was hardly a packing job. Nevertheless, Brown chided Sault residents for their lack of citizenship in permitting this outcome and claimed that only six permanent Sault men had attended the caucus. If so, four of the six voted for Chapel, who subsequently won election over his Whig opponent.[19]

Such a defeat must have rankled, for it was open proof of Brown's inability to influence his own townsmen. The officers of the Canal Company, meanwhile, had been clever enough to participate in local charities at the Sault and win the influence that Brown lacked. Harvey had solicited his directors for funds to help build a Presbyterian church, the first church of any denomination in the community. By the spring of 1855 the treasurer of the Presbyterian society could acknowledge gifts totaling $580 collected by Harvey from the directors. The church was debt free and under construction.

Such an accomplishment carried more weight with Sault residents that did Brown's various charges. The citizens of the Sault were more amused than annoyed at Harvey's timber-poaching activities. In the eyes of these westerners, it was respectable to help oneself to timber held in absentee ownership, as the Canal Company directors would soon learn to their regret. As to land fraud, since the average westerner in the 1850s thought that land resources were inexhaustible, the rejection of a few acres by the Canal Company in favor of better lands was not important. Again, Brown could charge manslaughter, but true westerners never got lost in the woods when the last boat was about to sail. Canal Company workers could even suffer and die of cholera, but in the eyes of the community, these were lowly immigrants paying the price of their own debauchery. The Sault people did not understand that the workers had brought the disease with them from Detroit. Finally, only a few may have realized that with the canal Sault Ste. Marie would stagnate through loss of the forwarding trade, for Brown had once said that with a canal the Sault could look forward to a growth equal to Detroit's.

Try as he might, Brown could not sustain a popular case at the Sault against the Canal Company, and in October he decided that he had had enough and launched an effort to sell the *Lake Superior Journal*. He offered, for $3,000, to dispose of the entire establishment, including type, press, an "extensive job office," lists of from eight to nine hundred subscribers, a list of advertisers, a complete back file, and goodwill. He suggested that the paper be moved to Marquette, Michigan, where he hinted that a down payment of $1,000 could be raised immediately from new subscribers, of whom he promised to find fifty during the coming winter. Finally, he realized that the *Journal's* stock of goodwill was in several places at a low level, and he openly admitted that new advertisers would come forth only if the paper acquired a new editor.[20]

8 Precarious Financing

While Harvey and Brooks struggled with the rapidly mounting difficulties at the Sault, Corning and Pruyn faced financing problems in Albany. All the Canal Company stockholders had paid $5 per share at the time of subscription, and Pruyn had issued his first call for an additional $5 on 23 June 1853. Further calls followed. In September, Pruyn announced that transfer books would soon be open, should a stockholder wish to sell part or all of his holdings. At the same time he called for $5 on 15 September and another $5 on 15 October, but even this was not nearly sufficient to meet the expenses that Harvey would incur at the Sault. Corning, who must have been shocked at the September report of Nichols, decided to try to borrow from his own stockholders in early November. Any stockholder who would pay all or part of his subscription in advance of the calls would receive 7 percent interest per year on the sum paid in excess of the call. With this notice went a call for $10 due 25 November and another $5 due 10 December. Thus in less than eight months the company required the stockholders to pay 35 percent of their subscriptions. Since the directors had decided to capitalize at the maximum permitted by law, $1,000,000, Corning demanded $350,000 in this short time period. At this rate canal costs would soon overtake Nichols's "worst contingency" estimate of $403,500 and Canfield's $557,700.[1]

Corning must have anticipated from his reports that canal expenses would mount rapidly in 1854. Up to 1 September 1853 Harvey had spent only $75,000, but over one-third of this amount, $29,000, was spent in August alone. Brooks also kept an account in Detroit, but his expenditures should not be as large as Harvey's. The major expenditure that Harvey reported from the Sault was for excavation. This item amounted to $11,979, less than 10 percent of the total excavation cost as estimated by Nichols, and represented another warning that the project was going too slowly. Harvey's other expenses included more than $4,800 for twenty-five horses and a cutter and more than $7,500 for boarding supplies. Everything was more costly at the Sault, since horses and food had to be shipped from Detroit. Corning, as he studied the reports, was wise to spread the stock calls out as much as possible so that the entire burden would not fall in 1854.[2]

Nevertheless, several stockholders felt the pinch of the demands from Pruyn. Brooks, who had once thought that he would need to pay no more than 20 percent of his 400 shares, was especially concerned. Finance was not Brooks's strong point (which was perhaps the reason why Forbes still retained tight control over the Michigan Central Railroad from Boston), and he had assumed that the Canal Company could borrow as much of the remaining 80 percent as was needed using the unpaid stock pledges and 600,000 acres of land as collateral. Now Brooks complained of the pressure. He wanted to sell 100 shares of his canal stock if he could get $60 per share, but he was becoming increasingly involved in Harvey's problems and could not attend to the matter in person. As an alternative he asked Corning if he could borrow $10,000 from Corning's bank in Albany, using his Michigan Central stock as collateral. Probably other stockholders were as hard-pressed as Brooks. In 1853 Forbes, Fairbanks, and Corning were involved in the financing of the Hanibal Railroad, and Joy faced calls not only on his Canal Company stock but also on his stock in the Chicago and Aurora Railroad and the Illinois Central Railroad. To add to the problem, some of the eastern stockholders were upset by the news reports from the Sault. There was a danger that Brown might win his campaign after all, and Fairbanks had to devote much time and energy to dispelling the stockholders' fears.[3]

As anticipated, the expenses for the project continued to rise at an alarming rate in 1854, considering what remained to be done. The Canal Company had opened a land office in Detroit under the general supervision of George Frost, and as early as May 1854, it recorded expenses of $108,366, including an expenditure of over

$6,500 to pay the legal fees to dissolve the injunctions of the previous year. Payments and advances to landlookers amounted to $1,314, although the major effort to locate land was yet to come. The general expenses of the land office ran to more than $23,800, and by 4 May almost $11,000 had been paid to obtain stone at Malden, a figure that would mount rapidly as the summer progressed.[4]

Harvey also reported heavy expenses at the Sault. As of 30 May 1854 he accounted for $385,442. The major item was still the cost of excavation, which he recorded at over $103,000. The increase in the working force was reflected in the cost of boarding the men, which now exceeded $62,000. Many teams were needed to haul building materials over the railroad and to furnish power to the cranes, and Harvey had paid over $17,000 for horses. Hauling, trimming, and placing the timber came to $26,598, and the masonry to more than $4,700, although on 30 May the masons had barely started work in the upper lock. Another item that would increase rapidly in the summer was the expense of freighting, which on 30 May stood at $21,697. Items that did not yet appear, because the work had not started on them, were the caisson gate and the underwater excavation. With one year's work still ahead, the cost had risen to within $18,000 of Nichols's estimate and $172,000 of Canfield's.[5]

Obviously more money would be needed in the treasury of the Canal Company, but Brooks continued to protest against further calls on his stock. From Corning's Albany City Bank he had obtained a sizable loan, which fell due in January. Corning covered for him. At the same time Brooks began to request the release of the grant lands to the company, despite the legal stipulation that the canal must first be completed and accepted. He insisted that the western stockholders had anticipated the early release of the land, although this must have been difficult for Corning to understand, since Joy had been present at the writing of the Michigan law. Harvey too was hard pressed to meet the payments on the stock allocated to him. He had invested $15,000 in the project to date, and this constituted his entire fortune. He had to ask Fairbanks to take charge of his personal finances, deposit bonds in his name if necessary, and sell 20 percent of his canal stock. "There is the most possibility," he wrote to Fairbanks, "that I shall need your kind offices in meeting canal assessments altho I shall try to use them as light as possible."[6]

Harvey was not in a good position to ask for favors, but Brooks was, considering all that Corning and Fairbanks expected of him. In their meeting of 15 January 1854, the directors decided to take advantage of the New York corporation law authorizing the Canal Company to assume a bonded debt not to exceed $250,000. The stockholders would be permitted to purchase $100 bonds of the company for $80. As Fairbanks later complained, the stockholders did not rush forward to seize the bargain, and for good reason. A railroad company, although it ran only fifty miles between two cities, would have real physical assets plus the chartered right to conduct its business. The Canal Company, however, had no physical assets at all, except for the *Dart*, tools, shanties, and some stolen timber. Its right to build the canal would expire in a little over a year, and there was a danger that the company, by then, would have nothing to show for all its expense and trouble. It had the expectation of owning 750,000 acres, but as yet it did not own one square foot of the land. Brown insisted that this expectation was a pipe dream, and if he, an on-the-spot observer, should prove to be correct, an investment in a Canal Company bond would be money thrown away.[7]

The company now reverted to its original policy of making calls on the stock, a development that brought a protest from Fairbanks, who thought he had taken a fair share of the bonds whereas others had not. He did not consider it fair that he must now meet a 20 percent assessment, due 1 June, after paying for the bonds. Correctly anticipating that the new tugs, added supervisors, and mounting costs in general would necessitate even further calls, he proposed an alternate scheme. Let Brooks, Joy, Seymour, Corning, Fairbanks himself, and perhaps two others form a confidential association that would then borrow to meet the combined assessments, using the Canal Company stock as collateral. Fairbanks even submitted a sample form that the association might use. The notes would be due 1 August 1856, with a yearly interest rate of 7 percent. The association would place 5,000 shares of Canal Company stock in the hands of trustees and expect to obtain a loan of $150,000. Fairbanks reminded Corning that the company must not underestimate the value of the lands if it ever got title to them, observing that "there is little doubt that we have in the mineral ranges a vast amount of valuable mines, the value of which has never been fully appreciated." He communicated his thoughts to Brooks as well as to Corning; Brooks jumped at the idea of avoiding further stock calls and urged Joy to join in such an association.[8]

Fairbanks continued to pursue his plan through the summer, as Pruyn warned that further stock calls would be required. The July meeting of the directors was held in Springfield, Massachusetts, for the convenience of Fairbanks and Forbes. Fairbanks officially offered his plan to the directors and was authorized to investigate further. He then wrote to banks in Boston, Springfield, and Hartford. These responded with an aggregate offer of between $70,000 and $75,000, and Fairbanks took the offers with him to the 31 October meeting of the directors in Albany. He got no further. Pruyn objected "in a most decided manner against giving his private endorsement, and stated his conviction that there was no other way but to make another call." Forbes agreed with Pruyn.[9]

It was possible that the Michigan Central trio was in better financial condition by the end of October than they had been in July, when Brooks had confided to Corning, "I am in need of the money and no time this summer to look for it for myself." During the critical years for Canal Company financing, 1854 and 1855, business editor and analyst Henry Varnum Poor noted that the Michigan Central had deviated from its usual practice. Up to this time Brooks and Forbes had provided complete reports for Poor to publish, but now their reports were entirely inadequate. Poor wrote that the railroad had continued to pay high dividends in 1854 and 1855 without any rise in gross receipts. Its construction account had increased $4,000,000, although it did not add a single mile to its system. Forbes made no report on reserves for depreciation, renewals, or contingencies. Poor was forced to assume that the high dividends were paid from capital rather than from profits.[10]

Whether or not there had been financial juggling on the Michigan Central, the Sault Canal was built at least in part with the railroad's profits. Three of the Canal Company's directors—Forbes, Brooks, and Corning—were major stockholders of the road, and it is probable that two more—Joy and Pruyn—held shares. Apparently John Seymour was also in a favorable financial position. During the spring and summer of 1854, he accepted at least three notes from his brother Horatio for a total of over $10,000.[11]

Having rejected Fairbanks's plan for raising additional funds, the directors decided that it would be necessary to explain the mounting cost of the work to the stockholders in order to prepare them for a further call on the stock. First, they listed the increased cost of provisions and labor. Then came the greatly increased transportation charges resulting from the failure to find suitable limestone for the locks within a reasonable distance. (The directors did not mention the Brown-Harvey dispute over the limestone on Drummond's Island.) Third, it was claimed—falsely—that ill health among the work force in the *first* year of construction had made it difficult to maintain an adequate supply of labor. The work force had, in fact, been decimated during the *second* season by the cholera epidemic that raged for eight or nine weeks. Finally, the directors warned the stockholders that the cost of exploring and evaluating the grant lands was higher than anticipated. All this was in preparation for the final blow; the work would use up almost all the company's capital.[12]

The directors now took the last step in financing the project. They instructed Pruyn to issue the final call on the stock, and he complied on 2 November. Fairbanks hinted his annoyance and assumed with some justification that Pruyn had spoken up at Corning's request. The final call had pushed even Fairbanks beyond his financial limit, and he wrote that he would have to borrow most of the sum.[13]

9 The Final Push

In January 1855 the directors of the Canal Company took drastic action. They had dealt successfully with the Michigan legislature in the past, and now they decided to appeal to that body for the immediate grant of the lands.

Apparently it was thought that Attorney General Howard, though still an enemy of the Canal Company, would have little influence on the lawmakers. Moreover, Corning and Pruyn finally secured the cooperation of Michigan's chief engineer, John Clark, who had returned to New York from Detroit for the winter. Clark agreed to submit a report to the legislature supporting the company's request. In preparing this report he must have used the figures and estimates of the Canal Company. He had not visited the project in November for a firsthand view, and Major Glenn would not have given him statistics favorable to the company. Corning committed one of his rare tactical errors when he permitted Clark to date his report from Albany. A Michigan enemy of the Canal Company could easily point out that Clark's home was in Utica, and that the report might just as well have been signed by Erastus Corning.[1]

In his report Clark stated that the canal followed specifications with one exception—the stones used in the lock backing were not as large as required. They were, however, the best the country afforded, and Clark assured the legislature that they had been placed with great care. The gates, he stated, had been built according to the design of Captain Canfield. He noted that "the great width of the chambers of the locks had rendered it difficult to devise a plan for the gates, capable of resisting the pressure of the water." Here

Clark either forgot his lessons in hydraulics or assumed that the legislature knew nothing about lock gates. The maximum pressure on a gate at any point is determined by the depth of the water held back and not by the canal width.[2]

Clark next listed the work that remained on 28 November 1854. This included 4,600 cubic feet of rock excavation in the canal itself and almost 6,000 cubic feet of underwater excavation. The caisson gate was not ready, and the lock gates were not set in place and painted. Clark estimated that the cost of work remaining would be $24,000.[3]

Finally Clark reported on all the extra work, not included in the contract, that the Canal Company had completed. This included excavation to enlarge a ship basin, special embankments, and additional masonry. The cost of the additional work amounted to $47,000, and Clark recommended that the company be paid that sum. Furthermore, since the value of the extra work exceeded the value of the contract work still to be done, Clark made the recommendation that Corning wanted: "It seems to be no more than just and reasonable, that the compensation named in the contract for the performance of same, should be rendered; and I am free to say, that such has been the uniform practice pursued in similar cases, on the public works of this, as well as other states, where I have had the supervision of them as engineer." With these words Clark signed his report, and Seymour prepared to take it to Lansing.[4]

Unfortunately for Corning, however, his Michigan enemies were hard at work in Lansing. Brooks, recovering from his illness in Detroit, was probably warned by Charles Chapel that there was trouble in Lansing. On 10 January he sent a peremptory telegram to Joy, who was attending to railroad business in Chicago: "Go directly to Lansing without coming here." Brooks could not participate himself because he was having his teeth pulled. Upon arrival in Lansing, Joy found that J. Venen Brown, Jacob Howard, and Samuel Whitney (the witness to Harvey's timber theft) were stirring up as much trouble for the Canal Company as possible. They had obtained the signatures of the majorities of both houses of the legislature to a petition calling upon Governor Bingham to replace Clark with Major Glenn as chief engineer for the state. The petition protested against Clark's appointment and reminded the governor that Glenn was "*a citizen of this state*." At the same time Brown and Whitney began their testimony before a senate select committee regarding Harvey's theft of timber from Section 16 land.[5]

Brooks was naturally alarmed at the turn of events. The substitution of Glenn for Clark at so critical a stage would seriously endanger the prospects of the Canal Company in Lansing, and Brooks above all others wanted the lands released at once. He urged that Corning call a directors meeting in Detroit to consider the emergency, and Corning agreed. On 24 January, Corning, Brooks, Fairbanks, and Seymour met in Detroit and decided to reinforce Clark's report with a petition to the governor and legislature requesting the immediate grant of the 750,000 acres. They also decided to call upon the aid of shipowner Eber Ward and former Detroit mayor Zach Chandler. Chandler gave Ward a letter of introduction to Governor Bingham, which stated that "Capt. Ward is of the opinion that the Canal Co. has had a pretty hard time and is entitled under all circumstances of the case to the lands immediately." Chandler denied that Ward had any financial interest in the Canal Company and noted that the shipper was ready to execute a $100,000 bond to add to the surety that the canal would be completed on time. The petition, Clark's report, and Chandler's letter were entrusted to Joy, Porter, Seymour, and Ward, since proper timing in Lansing was important. Friends of the Canal Company had placed a bill releasing the lands with a favorable senate committee, but the three canal men decided to delay action on the bill until the school land problem could be settled.[6]

Seymour's first responsibility lay with the governor, while Joy worked with the legislature. By 6 February, Seymour was able to notify his associates that Governor Bingham, resisting the petition of the legislature, would not replace Clark as chief engineer. In agreeing not to interfere, the governor assured Joy in front of witnesses that Clark would not be removed until after the canal was accepted. The saving of Clark was a major victory, but the fear persisted that Bingham might change his mind at a later date. Brooks, for one, considered Bingham a weak character easily dominated by Attorney General Howard, but Seymour realized that it would not do to irritate the governor with further pressure. It would, however, be possible to attack Howard and expose him as the legal counsel for Brown, should such a step become necessary.[7]

By the end of January, the select committee issued its report exonerating the Canal Company of responsibility for the timber theft. Joy and Seymour then decided to push the senate land bill through the legislature as quickly as possible. Seymour arranged for the printing of copies of Clark's report and the Canal Company's petition, all to be held for distribution. Bingham agreed to present the petition to the senate, but the canal men had not reckoned with Howard. On the night of Saturday, 3 February, the attorney general forced a meeting of the Michigan cabinet, which included the principal executive officers of the state. Whatever arguments Howard used, they were successful. The cabinet by unanimous vote overruled the governor on the immediate issue of the 750,000 acres. Faced with this show of solidarity, Bingham, Joy, and Seymour backed down. Defeat in the senate was now probable, and it would not be safe for the Canal Company to push Bingham any further against the wishes of all the other executive officers. Seymour discarded the company petitions, but permitted the submission of Clark's report to the senate; it could do no harm. Joy, Porter, Seymour, and Ward prepared to leave Lansing.[8]

Brooks was appalled at the turn of events. He wrote to Joy, "I can not abide the idea of not getting our lands if it is possible to get them. You must consider what will be the position of affairs if we *don't* get the canal done technically. There are many chances of this and you must look to that as a likely result." Joy, Porter, and Seymour, however, were pleased with their efforts. Seymour wrote that the state politicians were now aware that Howard was playing a dog-in-the-manger role. It could be recalled that Howard had acted for the Michigan Southern Railroad interests in obtaining the injunctions in early 1853. Now, as attorney general, he was also acting as Brown's legal counsel. It would only be necessary to apply counterpressure and establish Howard as Brown's attorney of record. Seymour noted one final accomplishment besides the saving of Clark. Someone at the Sault in November had had the presence of mind to take a number of daguerreotypes of the canal locks. These, together with face stone samples, were circulated in Lansing, and Seymour wrote that the pictures and samples impressed even the enemies of the Canal Company.[9]

The legislature had another chore that was not the concern of the Canal Company, which would no longer be responsible or even interested once Michigan accepted the completed canal. The lawmakers must provide for the administration of the canal according to federal law. On 12 February, Bingham signed the necessary legislation. It placed the general oversight of the canal in the hands of a board of control consisting of the governor, the auditor general, and the state treasurer. This body was charged with establishing the operating rules of the canal and the control of its funds. The law set the canal toll at 4¢ per ton for each ship's enrolled tonnage, but the board of control had the authority to revise this toll in the future. By federal law Michigan could charge only the amount needed to maintain the canal and pay for its supervision.[10]

More important, the Michigan law authorized the governor, with the consent of the senate, to appoint a supervisor of the canal at a salary not to exceed $1,500 per year for a two-year term of office. It would be the superintendent's responsibility to see that the tolls were properly paid, the canal kept in good order, and the rules established by the board of control enforced. The superintendent must keep a record of the names and types of vessels using the canal, the names of the captains, and the tonnage of each ship. For several years after the passage of the law, the superintendents exceeded these orders by enumerating the cargoes as well. Eventually, as canal usage increased, the latter practice had to be abandoned. Actually the job would not be an onerous one, at least for the first few years, since the superintendent was entitled to employ workers to handle the gates and attend to routine tasks. Sault editor Brown wanted the position and had Howard's backing with the governor as well as the support of a petition signed by thirty men. To the delight of Brooks, however, the governor rejected the advice of the attorney general and gave the job to John Burt. Brooks and Burt had maintained friendly relations during the years of construction, and Brooks considered the new superintendent to be fair and honest. By coincidence, sometime between November 1854 and May 1855, Burt and a Mr. Chase purchased the *Lake Superior Journal* from Brown. It is possible that Brown's failure to get the superintendent's job with its $1,500 salary was the determining factor in the sale. In any case, by May of 1855 the *Journal*'s drumfire of criticism directed against the Canal Company management was reversed, and Brown's career as a Sault editor was ended.[11]

In addition to their problems in Lansing, the Canal Company directors were concerned with the details of the anticipated transfer of lands from the public domain to the state of Michigan, and then, they hoped, to themselves. George Frost had taken to Washington the extensive list of lands the company had requested, and on 20 November 1854 he filed it at the Washington land office of the Department of the Interior. Everyone then waited impatiently for Commissioner John Wilson and Secretary McClelland to act. The secretary had ruled favorably on the disputed claims of Harvey and Brown ten months before, but, as usual, Brooks was worried. He had warned Fairbanks in July 1854 that Brown would attempt to block the grant in Washington. Now, in January 1855, while advising Fairbanks to say nothing in public, he informed the Vermonter that the Washington authorities were still delaying a decision.[12]

In his anxiety Brooks imagined demons where none existed. Since the Brown-Howard combination had been defeated in Washington the year before, the two men were now concentrating their efforts in Lansing. The problem in the land office in Washington had nothing to do with the conflict in Michigan. It was caused instead by the complicated nature of the Canal Company claims. It was necessary for clerks to check each individual claim against the records. No individual claim could be larger than one section (640 acres), and the Canal Company had made 1,422 claims in the Upper Peninsula alone. Many were for quarter-quarter sections of 40 acres, and some were for lots even smaller. Checking these would have been a time-consuming task in even a smoothly run office, and in early 1855 the Washington land office was not the best-administered department in the government. Its head was John Wilson, a Whig appointee of the previous administration whom Cass had persuaded Pierce and McClelland to retain because of his knowledge and efficiency. By 1855, however, Wilson was dabbling more and more in Know Nothing politics, and in June of that year Pierce would fire him. In spite of the confusion in Wilson's office, the Canal Company was actually fortunate. When Congress was not in session, Pierce proved to be an inveterate meddler in minor administrative details that should have been left to others. As the year progressed, he became involved in diplomatic reorganization, naval efficiency, and an alley fight between Winfield Scott and Jefferson Davis. To the advantage of the Canal Company, he permitted McClelland to run the Department of the Interior without interference.[13]

In February the Washington land office completed its work and sent the patents for 750,000 acres to Michigan over McClelland's signature. Brooks, who received certified copies from Washington, was pleased to note the accuracy with which George Frost had worked. Of the entire request only about 2,000 acres had been disallowed; these were found to be part of the "swamp lands" already granted to Michigan. For the time being the patents remained in the office of Michigan Secretary of State John McKinney, but Brooks, fearing a new wave of injunctions, was determined that there should be no delay in delivering them once the canal had been accepted. He noted that the standard Michigan patent forms could not be used since their forfeiture provisions would not apply to the canal grant lands because of their taxfree status. To expedite matters, Brooks volunteered the services of Frost to devise a new form that would be suitable for the unusual situation. The Michigan land office men, pleased at the opportunity to get out of an unpleasant job, accepted the offer. As Brooks told Fairbanks, "With all the papers ready for signature I think we can well say to the authorities 'as it will take but a little time to execute these papers please do so before asking us to surrender the canal!!' "[14]

In his eagerness to avoid delay, however, Brooks had overlooked an essential detail. The Michigan land office authorities quite properly insisted that the attorney general of the state approve the new patent forms as devised by Frost. The requirement gave Howard a fresh opportunity to cause trouble. He simply sat on the forms for weeks, doing nothing, and without his approval Frost could not begin the tedious process of listing the individual claims. When John Burt checked in behalf of the Canal Company, Howard replied that he could not make up his mind as to the legality of the forms. Furthermore, he questioned whether the proper assignment of the contract had been made from the New York incorporators to the directors of the Canal Company. Corning assured Bingham that the company was prepared to furnish proof "at any time and place it may reasonably be required to do so." Proof was indeed demanded, and Brooks and Joy forwarded the certified copy of the assignment to Bingham on 28 April. Next, the attorney general told Burt that he could not find the state's copy of the canal contract in Lansing. Brooks philosophized, "No legal paper can be so drawn that a lawyer intending to cavil at it will not find in it the means of disapproving of its form and its sufficiency for the purpose intended." At this point he feared that a writ of mandamus would be required before the Canal Company could get its lands.[15]

While Howard pretended indecision on the land forms, the Canal Company decided to apply counterpressure. On 19 March attorneys representing the company filed a complaint against Brown in circuit court in Detroit. For its legal action the company selected the firm of Lathrup and Duffield. Either Joy and Porter were too busy with the railroads, or it was decided to retain attorneys who had no interest in the canal. In its complaint the Canal Company demanded that Brown be ordered to surrender the limestone quarry on Drummond's Island. It was the contention of the company that Brown, acting as its agent, should have claimed and purchased the land for the company and not for himself. Harvey had sent Brown the commission of the governor designating Harvey as a canal land agent for Michigan, a letter deputizing Brown to the same office, and a blank land warrant. In his deposition Harvey swore that he had met Brown for the first time at the Sault in November 1852, and at that time they had discussed the availability of high-grade limestone for the canal. Harvey also made this statement: "I had charge of all of the company's land matters, financial matters, construction of the canal in the Upper Peninsula. It was also my province to appoint agents and others under myself." It was then safe for him to claim far more than his share of credit for the project, and he continued to do so for the rest of his life.[16]

The court issued a subpoena for Brown, now a resident of Wayne County, to appear 1 May 1855 to defend himself. The defendant retained the firm of Howard and Mandell to represent him, and Jacob Howard thus officially became attorney of record for Brown. With but one exception Brown agreed to the facts as stated in the complaint. He claimed that he did not realize that the Canal Company would require a great quantity of limestone, and that he had purchased the Drummond's Island quarry for himself rather than for the company. When he later discovered the need of the company, he offered to sell the limestone, but Harvey would agree to pay only a pittance. Brown claimed, correctly, that Harvey had no right to delegate his authority as state land agent. He went so far as to state that Harvey was not himself a legal land agent because his commission, though signed by Governor Parsons, lacked the seal of the State of Michigan. Brown testified that he did not have a binding contract with the company until June 1853, when Harvey hired him for $2,000 to look after the company land interests. He stated that prior to the contract he had had no legal responsibility to the company and that after the contract he had acted in good faith as the company's agent. He did not defend himself regarding his claim of the access land on Drummond's Island in November 1853, when his contract was still in force.[17]

The case dragged on until the summer of 1856 and never reached a conclusion. The court received the deposition of Joseph Kemp, who stated that Brown had hired him to look for suitable limestone as early as November 1852. Kemp's testimony, along with letters introduced as evidence by the plaintiff and signed by Brown, refuted Brown's defense based on ignorance of the need for limestone. Sault land agent Warner testified as to the circumstances of Brown's claiming the access land under the noses of Harvey and Brooks in November 1853. The presentation was sufficient for the officers of the Canal Company, and they stopped the proceedings against Brown. They had more land than they knew what to do with, and they could afford to let Brown keep his quarry, for all the good it would do him. What was more important, they had accomplished their purpose. They had brought pressure on Brown and Howard at the proper time, and they had formally established Howard's affinity with Canal Company enemies. Any official act of the attorney general would be viewed in that light.[18]

On New Year's Day in 1855 Harvey submitted his regular report, this time with a warning note. There was ice in the canal, and it was not caused by freezing rain or snow but by water seeping through the banks of the canal from the river. By February, Harvey realized the significance of this seepage. The problem was the river cove, the risk that Canfield had been forced to accept in October 1852. Harvey warned Seymour that the canal banks were weak for a distance of about four hundred feet above the upper lock. Along this length the proposed water level in the canal (the level of Lake Superior) would be above the level of the land. The canal water would be retained by the banks already constructed. However, the bottom of the canal would be below the water level of the river. Thus a double danger threatened. When the canal was drained, water from the river might force a breach in the banks. When the canal was filled, water might break out in the reverse direction. In either case the bank might progressively crumble under the pressure of the water until the lock masonry was reached. Heavy pressure on the side of the masonry thus exposed might wash it away as well and destroy the entire canal; even the village itself could be flooded. Harvey asked that Seymour notify Clark of the danger, although technically, the company was safe because the banks had been built to greater thickness than specified.[19]

In spite of the risks, Harvey hoped to fill the canal in early spring. He had a good reason: the dredge had completed most of its work on Lake Superior, and he wanted it moved to the lower end. He proposed to set the upper caisson gate in place, use the dredge to break up the upper cofferdam, and then open the valves of the gate to admit the water slowly. He would then pass the dredge down through the canal and close the caisson gate again. Not wanting to take sole responsibility for this maneuver, he asked Seymour to consult with Clark as to alternative courses of operation. Clearly Harvey had at least listened to Canfield's warning against removing the cofferdam until the canal was protected in some way. Moreover, the situation forced him to evaluate the work progress at the upper caisson gate, and he was not pleased with what he found.[20]

Up to this point Harvey had usually been willing that Seymour show his letters to Clark so that responsibility could be shared. Whenever he discovered that a serious error had been made by the Canal Company, however, he warned Seymour to show the letter reporting it only to those on "our side." The situation at the upper caisson gate was such a case.

As designed by Canfield and constructed by the company, the gate was a huge, watertight box, seventy feet long, crossing the canal completely. Its width, eight feet at the bottom, tapered to three feet at the top. It was fourteen feet high. When towed into place and filled with water, the gate would form an effective dam across the canal. It would hold 3,080 cubic feet of water weighing over ninety-six tons. When it was time to fill the canal, sluice gates near the bottom of the caisson would let water through the gate. Then the gate would be pumped free of water and towed aside to a niche in the canal wall for storage. The chief problem was that the gate would have to fit perfectly between the canal walls and make a watertight juncture with the canal bottom.[21]

The sill upon which the gate would rest when in use was thus of considerable importance. Canfield ordered that heavy transverse timbers be set two feet apart in hydraulic mortar. Each timber would span the width of the canal, and each timber end must extend four feet under the masonry sides of the canal. The timbers must be dressed to a width of ten inches on the top and twelve or fourteen inches on the bottom so that the weight of the mortar would hold them down. Planking two and one-half inches thick could then be spiked to the timbers to form a floor upon which the caisson would rest.[22]

The trouble came in the execution of Canfield's orders. The sill could not be prepared until the excavation had been completed, and the excavation at the upper end of the canal had fallen behind schedule. As a result the carpenters could not set the timbers until after the first severe frost. Harvey reported to Seymour that the mortar had not set properly because of the cold weather, and he feared that the caisson gate would afford no protection once the upper cofferdam was removed. The water would flow as freely as ever under the gate. Harvey therefore asked the directors to obtain an extension of time for the completion of the canal. He proposed to scrape away the ice and lay several canvas sails over the sill in the hopes of obtaining a watertight fit. Then, if the directors could obtain an extension, a proper mortar job could be done in the spring. At the same time Harvey asked for instructions so that he could move the dredge through the canal. On this point he warned Seymour, "And let him [Clark] refer as little to Col. Glenn's judgement as possible as the Col is bound not to have us get through our job in time if he can block the game in any way."[23]

Once again Harvey proved his ineptitude as an engineer and planner. He had not learned from Brooks's statement that it would not do to let one part of the work get in the way of another. Harvey proposed to use the dredge to break up the upper cofferdam and then to pass the dredge through the canal. In practically the same breath, he proposed to do a proper mortar job on the caisson sill the following spring. But, with the upper cofferdam gone, the sill would be under a minimum of ten feet of water! It was also difficult to see what sail canvas would do that planking would not accomplish. If the timbers were washed away because of mortar failure, the canvas would go too. Finally, Harvey should have been aware that neither Clark, the canal commission, nor the governor had the power to extend the completion date. The job simply had to be finished by 19 May.

All this presented another problem for Brooks, and to add to the trouble, he was now getting conflicting reports from the Sault. It was understandable that nerves would fray on the project. Harvey and Nichols were completing their second winter of working together, and Nichols had lost all patience with the younger man. Harvey announced that excavation would be completed on 1 April, and Nichols believed that he had the responsibility to warn Brooks not to place any confidence in Harvey's statement. Referring to his own report, he called the 1 April date ridiculous. Nichols also warned Brooks that Harvey, acting as a "higher law," was directing the men to proceed rapidly while ignoring the canal's weak spots. There was at least one point that Harvey had pronounced finished that would never pass inspection, and Nichols feared that warm weather would reveal others. He also complained of Harvey's sarcastic criticism of his foremen and of the unfair demands he placed on everyone.[24]

Brooks needed no reminder of Harvey's mistakes; the man's record was now a long one of overoptimistic reports and failed promises. It would never do to permit him to hide shoddy work in the hope that it would not be discovered later. Nevertheless, he would have to be handled with tact, at least until the navigation season opened. After all, Harvey was on the scene and Brooks was not, the same situation that existed between Brooks and Forbes regarding affairs of the Michigan Central. The result was a long and carefully worded letter of advice regarding the caisson gate and its sill.

First Brooks told Harvey that he must not let the water into the canal until Clark had inspected the work. The order was quite reasonable, for Clark would want to inspect the lock floors and could not do so if they were underwater. Brooks realized that the timing would present a problem for Harvey, since the project could not be considered complete without the removal of the upper cofferdam. The sequence meant that the caisson gate had to be in place and functioning on the day when Clark and the commissioners arrived to inspect. Clark had not been told of the problem with the caisson gate sill.[25]

Brooks then offered Harvey three alternatives. If Harvey thought that the leakage problem would be minor, he could attempt a quick patchwork. If Harvey thought the problem more serious, he should leave the caisson gate in its place. Then, after removing all men and tools from the canal, he should test the caisson by lettering the water in through a special cut. The cofferdam must not be touched, and the cut must be such that it could quickly be filled again should the sill leak badly. In that case he should repair the leak and test again with the cut. If Harvey thought this solution hopeless because of the condition of the sill, Brooks offered a final plan. The most dangerous spot of all in the sill would be the area immediately in front of the transverse timber lying closest to Lake Superior. Brooks proposed that Harvey excavate a trench directly in front of this timber about two feet deep and three feet wide across the width of the canal. This trench would then be filled with six courses of brick mortared together in a terrace pattern with the widest terrace at the bottom to support the work. The entire terrace must then be covered with mortar to the level of the bottom of the canal.[26]

There were several advantages to the last plan. Even if the covering mortar did not hold well, the bricks would prevent water from working under the timber and washing it out. As to the stability of the brick structure, Brooks had to rely on the principle that many alternating joints in the structure would provide sufficient elasticity in freeze and thaw. Brooks tried to encourage Harvey by telling him that this same plan had worked under the Charlestown drydock in Boston harbor. If Harvey had no bricks, Brooks would try to get him some in the spring, time permitting. Otherwise, Harvey could use medium-size stones, but these must be handset in mortar as close together as possible. Above all, Brooks warned, the caisson gate must be watertight. It would be the only way that the canal could be protected during repair in future years once the cofferdam was gone. Brooks also realized that Clark's orders would prevent the dredge from leaving Lake Superior. Harvey must not worry about that. Clark would permit dredging below the canal after the deadline, on the grounds that his order had made the dredging impossible before then.[27]

The letter, which included a rough sketch of the brick work, contained not the slightest note of criticism and offered several words of encouragement. Brooks had given Harvey three alternatives to meet all eventualities and had then permitted the young man to use his own judgment. He did take the precaution of sending a copy of his letter to Fairbanks, along with a copy of Nichols's angry letter of 4 March, and he advised Fairbanks that he had told Harvey to be careful.[28]

It was all to no avail. Harvey snapped back that he could not carry out Brooks's instructions and that he had no time to give his reasons. To Fairbanks he wrote, "It is impossible for a man to sit in his office in Detroit and tell us explicitly how to carry on work here under all circumstances." He concluded, "If any adverse event should occur to frustrate our hopes I am inclined to believe that there would be a great 'shaking of skirts' & that the blame would all concentrate on my head right or wrong." The sail canvas would have to do, a decision that gave the directors something new to worry about. Harvey, with no engineering training, did not realize that the juncture between the caisson gate and its sill must be absolutely watertight. If water seeped under the gate, it would destroy the safety factor in Canfield's design by exerting a buoyant pressure on the gate equal to the weight of the water above it in the canal.[29]

Harvey also reported to Fairbanks that he had personally wheeled the last barrow load out of the cut on 6 April; still, Brooks's anxiety reached a new height. He had no way of knowing that this time Harvey was telling the truth. He sent urgent messages to Fairbanks no fewer than five times between 18 April and 3 May, reminding the former governor of the importance of his presence in Michigan in May. Brooks wanted the directors to meet at the Sault in advance of the canal commission to form plans of action should Harvey contrive further misadventures. With a faith in the weather not shared by the western men, Corning and Pruyn issued a call for a directors meeting at Sault Ste. Marie on Friday, 11 May 1855, or as soon thereafter as a quorum should arrive. Fairbanks was as much on edge as Brooks, probably because of the urgency of Brooks's letters, and promised to be ready when the first boat left for the Sault. Then, to the consternation of all, he suddenly changed his mind and announced that he could not leave the East. His brother Joseph was dying, and he had to suggest that Corning and Seymour make the trip without him.[30]

There was nothing left to do but wait for the weather to clear the ice out of the St. Mary's River. Brooks had warned Fairbanks that there was more ice than usual in Lake Huron and that the opening of navigation would be late. He even contemplated going north in April but concluded that he could not run the risk of getting stuck in the ice. Harvey had estimated that the ice would break up between 1 May and 5 May, and the first hopeful sign was observed on 2 May when a ship arrived in Detroit from Lake Michigan, indicating that the Straits of Mackinac were clear of ice. Finally, on 5 May, the impatient Brooks wired Corning that the steamers *North Star* and *Illinois* had come down from the Sault. The *Illinois* would return on 8 May, and Brooks wanted the directors and, above all, Clark to be aboard. If the trip took the usual three days, Brooks would have eight days to correct any new Harvey blunders and to add what finishing touches were necessary.[31]

Before leaving Albany, Corning learned that Clark, because of an injury during the previous fall, could not keep his promise to inspect the canal. The company was thus in the same position it had been in at the time of the death of Canfield. It was intolerable that Glenn should become chief engineer; Corning had to find a substitute for Clark. Fortunately one was available, the distinguished civil engineer William J. McAlpine, former state engineer and surveyor for the state of New York. Brooks had wanted McAlpine for the job in the first place, and McAlpine agreed to take Clark's place on the inspection trip.[32]

When the *Illinois* arrived at the Sault on 11 May, the new owners of the *Lake Superior Journal* were on hand, one of them ready to assume the responsibility for the canal as soon as the state took over. They were friends of the Canal Company and found little to criticize and much to praise. They reported that Brooks had to attend to one small leak in the canal bank before the contract expired. They also reported general frustration when, on contract day, 19 May, only one canal commissioner had arrived. By 21 May all were finally present except for former governor John Barry. The visiting group also included Governor Bingham, Attorney General Howard, Secretary of State John McKinney, Auditor General Whitney Jones, former congressman David Stuart, and Zach Chandler. All carefully inspected the work; the commissioners would not comment to the editors of the *Lake Superior Journal*, but the latter thought that the visitors looked satisfied. Their missions completed, the commissioners and canal officers then boarded the *Illinois* to return to Detroit.

The editors were correct. Before the *Illinois* had steamed far down the St. Mary's River, the governor and commissioners handed Corning a document second in importance only to the land patents:

> We . . . do hereby certify that a ship canal has been constructed around the Falls of St. Mary in the State of Michigan by the St. Mary's Falls Ship Canal Company. . . . That said canal has been constructed within two years within the making of the contract for the construction of said canal, to our satisfaction and acceptance.

> Kinsley S. Bingham
> Shubal Conant
> C. Joslin
> Henry Ledyard
> Alfred Williams

The same Michigan officers also certified that the original contractors with the state of Michigan had assigned all rights, privileges, and remunerations to the New York-based Canal Company. This ended the responsibility of the canal commission, and tensions lessened aboard the *Illinois*. They did not entirely disappear, however. Seymour foolishly interrupted McKinney on a matter of canal business while the latter was engrossed in the important business of a euchre game; the result was an exchange of harsh words between McKinney and Corning. This was unfortunate, since one more important step remained to be taken: McKinney still had in his office in Lansing the seal of the state of Michigan needed to complete the transaction.[33]

Fairbanks joined his fellow directors in Detroit when they returned from the successful Sault trip. His brother Joseph had died on 15 May, and the former governor could now carry his share in the effort to obtain the land. The directors agreed that speed was important. They did not want to fight a new series of injunctions from Brown or Sherman, nor did they want to initiate mandamus proceedings. Therefore they decided to launch a public appeal, should the state officers balk at transferring the land. Corning, meanwhile, prepared a lengthy letter addressed to Bingham, McKinney, and the commissioner of the State Land Office, S. B.

Treadwell, in which he reminded the officers that the canal had been satisfactorily completed and so certified by the governor, by the commissioners, and by McAlpine acting for Clark.[34]

Corning first wrote that it was common knowledge that canal enemies had attempted to defeat the award of the land and to reverse the approval of the secretary of the interior in order to claim the lands for themselves. They had been turned back, however, after a full hearing in Washington. Corning then anticipated his opponents' next step by stating that they had attempted to obtain injunctions to prevent the conveyance of the land to the Canal Company. He made the further assumption that several state officers would question the regularity of the grant from the United States to Michigan and decline to issue the patents on that ground. Corning insisted that while the state of Michigan held the land in fee simple, it now did so as the trustee for the Canal Company. He would be willing for a third party mutually agreed upon to hold the land in escrow, but he wanted to avoid litigation that would prove vexatious to the state. Finally Corning made the official request for the lands and concluded, "We have no reason from our past experience to expect favor or friendship from the state, . . . and no doubt every just and fair minded man, will probably appreciate the motives as well as the wisdom of the policy which compels us to *hold the canal.*"[35]

It was a clever letter in several respects. When Corning announced the company's intention to hold the canal, he knew who held the whip handle. The navigation season had opened, yet the Canal Company had no authority to operate the canal for Great Lakes shipping. Corning could order the upper caisson gate closed and the canal drained—and then sit back to watch the fun. McKnight, Ward, and the rest of the shipping industry would join the numerous mining enterprises, the Detroit merchants, and the fishing industry in descending with rage upon the Michigan authorities. Democratic politicians ousted from office in 1854 by the upstart Republican party of Michigan would have a grand issue. Further, Corning cleverly referred to the canal enemies rather than to the enemies of the Canal Company. He was quite aware that no one of importance in Michigan was an enemy of the canal itself, and a slight twisting of words thus united his interests with the state's against a common foe. Finally, Corning signed the letter as president of the company, along with the two Michigan men who were his associates. The two easterners, Fairbanks and Seymour, whose names had political associations, did not sign.

Corning ordered that copies be made for general distribution if necessary, and the men dispersed for the next phase of the operation. Fairbanks and Seymour departed for Lansing at once, with Corning's letter and a somewhat subdued attorney general. Brooks hurried off to retrieve the land certificates that he had hidden in or near Detroit. He would follow his associates as soon as he could. Frost was already in Lansing talking to the state officials; and Corning, with his usual confidence in his directors, left for Albany.[36]

In 1855 there was no railroad between Detroit and Lansing, and Fairbanks, Seymour, and Howard rode the entire eighty miles in a wagon over a rough log road, arriving in the capital at 3:00 A.M. on 25 May. Perhaps Howard had been swayed by his visit to the canal, and perhaps he was impressed when Corning, in Detroit, confided to him that he must go to Lansing with the canal men to safeguard the interests of Michigan. It was also likely that the attorney general, an astute politician destined to reach the United States Senate, realized that a company about to take possession of 750,000 acres of Michigan land might be a power to reckon with in the future. Whatever the case, Seymour reported that Howard appeared to act in good faith and did not object to a word in any of the legal documents presented to him for approval.[37]

When the day's work began that Friday in Lansing, Fairbanks turned his attention to the state officers, trying to win their support for what Seymour called a "Fairbanks Platform." He reminded Howard that in the eyes of the general public the attorney general exercised control over state secretary McKinney. The public therefore would hold Howard responsible for whatever decision was reached. Seymour, meanwhile, joined Frost and the state land office clerks in the tedious job of comparing the United States grants to Michigan with the copy of the Canal Company claims that Frost had brought to Lansing. Before the job was finished, Seymour felt that his tongue had been as completely quartered as a section of 640 acres. He also managed, at least in part, to make up with McKinney for the angry exchange aboard the *Illinois*, although the secretary was by no means converted to the cause of the Canal Company.[38]

Shortly after 4:00 P.M. Brooks arrived with the certificates, having made record time from Detroit. Howard escorted McKinney to the secretary's office, where the two men began to sign and seal the certificates and patents, dealing first with the mineral lands, and then with the pinelands. By 7:30 P.M. they were done, and Mc-Kinney delivered all 750,000 acres to Brooks and Seymour. With the lands safely in the possession of the Canal Company, Seymour handed the written transfer of the canal itself to McKinney. This paper was the last to change hands, and the job was done.

Seymour reported that once the transaction was completed the Michigan officials suddenly became great friends with the canal men, behaving with as much cordial enthusiasm as if they had won the grant lands themselves. The next day they all rode together in the company's wagon to the Michigan Central lines at Jackson, where Brooks generously distributed passes on the road to the Michigan men. Brooks, Fairbanks, Seymour, and Frost then returned to Detroit to receive congratulations from all except Abner Sherman, who by this time probably wanted to separate the Upper Peninsula from the Union. A banquet followed in honor of the governor, the former governors, and the canal officers, and by 30 May the patents rested safely in the care of Pruyn in Albany. When Fairbanks delivered them, Seymour thought he heard Corning say, "All right."[39]

10 Counting the Cost and Operating the Canal

Only a handful of Sault citizens, mostly bartenders mourning their lost clientele, and some passengers were on hand to witness one of the great events in industrial history. There was no DeWitt Clinton to pour a keg of Lake Superior water into the St. Mary's River, and the marquis de Lafayette, who had graced the opening of the Erie Canal, had been dead for twenty-one years. The canal builders, officers and laborers, had all departed. Gone too were the men, now redundant, of the freight forwarding business, when the first ship locked through to Lake Superior. It was the *Illinois*, returned from the lower Great Lakes on 18 June 1855 with cargo and passengers for the upper lake. What were the thoughts of the hardened miners as they crowded the bows to watch the locks operate? "A great moment in history"? No. More likely, "It's damn well about time." An event of even greater significance took place two months later in view of an even smaller audience. The brigantine *Columbia*, three days out of Marquette, locked through the canal with 132 tons of red iron ore mounded on her deck. Escorted by Lady Elgin, the canal mule and essential consort for sail vessels in the canal, the *Columbia* was destined for the Cuyahoga River and the Cleveland-Cliffs Iron Company. This was the first shipment in a trade that would reach an annual 100 million tons a century later.[1]

Michigan now owned the canal and would own and operate it for the development of the Upper Peninsula and Minnesota until 9 June 1881, when the United States took over. In return the United States and Michigan had released 750,000 acres, or slightly more than two percent of the total land surface of the state. In comparison

Michigan under the Morrill College Land Grant Act of 1862 received 240,000 acres, all located within the state, for higher education. The Canal Company had made its selections a decade before and, as will be seen, had chosen wisely. Higher education in Michigan was the loser in these transactions, and it would be well to see what Michigan bought for so high a price.

Strictly speaking, the canal was not built to specifications. The sill under the upper caisson gate was in questionable condition and remained a potential danger as long as the Michigan authorities relied upon the gate for protection. There was an obvious reason why McAlpine and the commission accepted the sill, sailcloth and all—they never saw it! Since Clark had insisted on inspecting the canal before the water was let in, the caisson gate completely covered the sill. It could not be moved after the breakup of the upper cofferdam without flooding the canal contrary to Clark's orders. When the canal was filled and the caisson gate towed to storage, the sill was out of sight under twelve feet of water. If Major Glenn had protested, it would have been his word against that of Brooks, Harvey, Nichols, Corning, and Seymour. Possessed of such a preponderance of dignity and authority (Harvey excepted), the Canal Company never had to argue at a disadvantage either at the Sault or in Lansing.[2]

The work, although nearly finished, had not been completed by 21 May. The Canal Company entered an agreement with the commissioners to complete the job after acceptance, and the total cost came to but $1,812.96. No steps were taken to remedy the weakness in the canal bank just west of the lock masonry, which would cause trouble in the future. However, the embankments had been built to specifications, and, contrary to Brown's dire predictions, the lock walls survived the winter of 1854–55 as well as subsequent winters.[3]

No innovations were built into the Sault canal. The obvious reason was that Canfield, who had done most of the engineering work, had had no previous canal experience. When in doubt, he usually copied the methods used on the Erie Canal, although his plans for sandbar protection reflected knowledge gained in his own general line of work. Nichols, though familiar with canal engineering, did not tamper with Canfield's design because Brooks would not permit it. Thus several unsatisfactory features of the Erie

Canal were built into the Sault as well. For example, Canfield
adopted the standard Erie method of filling and emptying the locks.
A series of small sluice gates ran along the bottom of each lock gate.
They were opened and closed by a butterfly valve system that could
be operated by a gateman who turned a crank and rotated a
horizontal shaft that ran the length of the gate. Through a simple
gear arrangement, the shaft raised or lowered vertical shafts going
down to each sluice gate. The raising operation brought a panel in
the sluice gate parallel to the force of the water and opened the
sluice. The lowering operation brought the panel parallel to the gate
surface and closed the sluice. The system did not affect the physical
strength of the gate itself, since the structural members were not
involved. However, it did decrease the hydrostatic strength and
permitted an annoying turbulence in the lock that had also plagued
the Erie locks. Moreover, there was the inherent problem that if one
of the sluice gates should be jammed in an open position, all gates
would remain open, since they all operated off the same horizontal
shaft.[4]

John Burt, who inherited his father's inventiveness, solved these
problems too late for the Sault canal. During his term as canal
superintendent, he noted the objectionable turbulence that rocked
the boats. He knew how solidly the lock bottoms had been built, and
perhaps he wondered if such heavy construction had been necessary.
In any case, he devised a system for filling and emptying the locks
through a series of pipes running along the bottom. It worked like a
modern buried lawn sprinkler system, except that the outlets were
closer together and the water passed both ways.[5]

Canfield solved the problem of the weight of his gates by
supporting the far end of each from the bank with massive iron rods.
Turnbuckles held the rods in constant tension and relieved the
horizontal frame members of some of the sheer load. The
arrangement was effective, but it could hardly be called a major
innovation. The practice of mitering lock gates, or designing each
lock gate with a variable thickness to accommodate stress with a
minimum of gate weight, did not develop until after the Civil War.[6]

The caisson gate was an innovation, perhaps, but it was also one
of man's most cumbersome inventions. The enormous box had to fit
snugly against the sides of the canal and rest firmly on the bottom.
Anyone who has tried to fit a modern refrigerator into a niche in a

built-in kitchen will understand the problem. Not only must the dimensions be correct but the refrigerator must also be in a perfect upright position and absolutely level. The caisson gate presented even further complications. According to the principle of Archimedes, when water was pumped out of the gate preparatory to moving it to storage, the gate itself would slowly rise but the water within it would remain at a constant though slightly lower level than the water outside in the canal. Raise the gate high enough, and it would become a perfect sail, catching the slightest wind. One of the first warnings issued by Burt concerned the problem of protecting the canal should a violent storm come up at night. He could not set the caisson gate in place in the dark in a heavy wind. Burt's successor, Elisha Calkins, considered the caisson gate useless. By 1857 it had been badly damaged, and Calkins asked that a regular set of gates be installed to protect the works.[7]

None of these problems concerned the Canal Company stockholders, who at their annual meeting in 1855 reelected the same board of directors. It was discovered that James Joy had managed to sell all his stock before the acceptance of the canal, but Corning's partner Gilbert Davidson transferred five shares of stock to Joy so that the lawyer would be eligible to remain a director; Pruyn commented that Joy could resign if he did not like the idea. Joy's attitude was shared by several of the canal men. With only a dim idea of the value of the lands they now held, they wanted to sell as soon as possible and put their funds to work in other enterprises. Brooks and Harvey were still financially squeezed, and the latter gave Corning his power of attorney so that Corning could sell his stock to one of the Thayer brothers. Fairbanks had offered to help make a profit on the stock, but Harvey thought that he could "turn over money" better himself and was eager to sell at par. Brooks had a $10,000 note fall due at Fairbanks's St. Johnsbury bank in April. Forbes sent half the sum, and Brooks gave Fairbanks a four-month personal note for the rest. The annual meeting was also the time to reward faithful friends. Chapel already had a gold watch, and now Brooks gave Deodatus Whitwood ten paid-up shares of Canal Company stock, which by August of 1855 was selling for $107 a share.[8]

The company's officers now faced the job of counting the final cost of the project. The largest work force employed at any time was about 1,700 during the fall of 1854, when the call was for "men, men!" The company also used about one hundred horses and twenty-five head of cattle. The great shipping effort of 1854 required the use of twenty-five schooners, six barges, and four steam tugs. Nearly 150 tons of iron had gone into the canal, most of this coming from Corning's Albany Iron Works. Against the rock formation at the Sault, the Canal Company burned 3,157 kegs of blasting powder and required 4 1/2 tons of steel drills. Almost 200,000 cubic feet of heavy timber went into the foundation, gates, and piers, and 1 1/3 million square feet of planks were used for a multitude of purposes.[9]

Naturally, these materials cost far more than originally estimated, and it took several months before all the canal expenses could be totaled. The company officers attempted to separate canal costs from other items of expense incurred, although to do so was difficult with the figures from the Sault office. The expenses of excavation and building earth walls were the greatest items, amounting to almost double the cost of any other single operation. The total was finally set at above $403,000, almost exactly the amount that Nichols had estimated for the entire project and about four-fifths of Canfield's total estimate. The next most expensive item was the lock masonry, which cost almost $250,000. This included the cost of quarrying and freighting from Malden, and neither Nichols nor Canfield had anticipated hauling face stone from such a distance. The piers cost almost $68,000, the only major item that Canfield overestimated.[10]

Nichols received $7,739 for his arduous two years on the project. The Canal Company paid Michigan $19,982 for the services of state engineers. Assuming that Canfield received only his regular army pay, this was an exorbitant sum for Glenn's services and the brief episodes with Clark and McAlpine. The company also paid $33,522 in salaries to Harvey, Chapel, Whitwood, and others; to Brooks for his summer's work; and to Seymour for finding labor.[11]

The Canal Company was also forced to pay sums to landlookers to locate the best lands available for claim in both peninsulas in Michigan. Neither Canfield nor Nichols had taken this expense into account, and there was no reason why they should have done so; the item was not, strictly speaking, a canal building expense. The cost of locating land came to above $86,000, however, of which more than $77,000 was spent in the Lower Peninsula. If this item is set aside, the cost of building the canal at Sault Ste. Marie was $913,492.15.[12]

The Canal Company's expenses did not stop with the acceptance of the canal by Michigan. Although the lands granted were free from taxation for five years, the costs of surveying and maintenance began to mount immediately. In the first two years of ownership, the Detroit land office of the Canal Company paid more than $53,000, and the land agency at Marquette paid more than $29,000. During the same period the company sold only $37,300 worth of land. Company records also indicate that some of the stockholders failed to pay the full assessment on their shares; the account was short almost $78,000. Meanwhile, the company had succeeded in selling only $190,000 of the authorized $250,000 of its bonds. At the end of the two years, it had a cash balance of only $13,425. This sum was held in the Albany City Bank, of which Erastus Corning was president. The choice was not coincidental; although the bank was sound enough, Corning would certainly profit from the investment of the Canal Company cash.[13]

Several factors accounted for the high cost of the canal, but one item can be dismissed at once. Harvey's dawdling in 1853 seriously jeopardized the organization as far as completion on time was concerned, but it did not add substantially to the cost of excavation. The project required 320,595 man-days, and it did not matter in which year the men worked. In 1854 there was no such thing as overtime pay, nor was the pittance paid to men like Knoblock for locating labor during that year's emergency significant in the total cost. Harvey's major contribution to the cost lay in permitting the quarrel with Brown to develop, thereby depriving the Canal Company of its source of prime limestone on Drummond's Island. The cost of frieghting from Malden was never listed as a separate item in the company's published reports, but it must have represented a major portion of the cost of the lock masonry. It would have been better for the Canal Company if Harvey had admitted that he had been fooled by the clever editor and paid Brown's price. In addition, the quarrel stimulated Brown's paper war, which hurt the financing efforts of the men in the East.

The isolated nature of the project as a cost factor worked both ways. It was costly to bring men, food, and tools to the Sault; but, once there, the men stayed for the season with no temptation to wander off in search of other jobs, relying on the Canal Company to return them to Detroit in the late fall. The cholera epidemic added somewhat to the cost, as Seymour had to replace the dead and sick men, but the transportation expense involved was not a major item.

In the long run neither mismanagement nor location accounted for the high cost of the canal. It was, rather, in the excavation cost that the company officers were misled. Canfield had all but used the word *guess* in his estimate, and Nichols had warned that the company could expect to find granite. In later years the company complained that it had been forced to excavate an additional foot beyond that required by the contract. The reason was not so much engineering error as general disagreement over the real surface level of Lake Superior—a matter of guesswork, inasmuch as the first geodetic survey of the western Great Lakes was not made until the early 1860s by an army captain named George Gordon Meade. Less than two months after Michigan took custody, the water level in the canal rose to a depth of fourteen feet, two inches.[14]

In retrospect the project was threatened more by a lack of time than a shortage of funds, in spite of the squeeze on Brooks. Once Corning realized the seriousness of the situation in the fall of 1853, he took prompt steps to increase the rate of call on the stock; and through this practice and the sale of bonds, the Canal Company managed to raise over $1,123,000.

Harvey was the individual most responsible for a situation that might have been disastrous, but others too were at fault. Nichols had estimated that the work season at the Sault was nine months per year, when seven would have been more accurate. Moreover, he assumed that each laborer would work 300 days per year and thus thought that the excavation could be completed by 325 men working eighteen months. It was to Nichols's credit that he was the first to realize the danger and issue a warning cry in late 1853. Had the company officers then listened to Harvey rather than to Nichols, the work would not have been completed on time.

The principal directors were also to blame for their inattention in 1853. Corning, Pruyn, Brooks, Joy, and Forbes were all preoccupied with railroad affairs. Fairbanks was serving his year as governor of Vermont, and Seymour was attending to the family farms during his brother's term as governor of New York. Fairbanks's defeat for reelection was the company's greatest stroke of luck in two years of construction. If he had not been free to bring order to the supervision of the project, a task that Corning was unwilling or unable to do, the work would not have been completed in contract time. Fairbanks was also in the best position to demote Harvey, since he was responsible for the young man in the first place.

Since Harvey outlived all the Canal Company directors, he was able to claim credit that should have been given to others. It was true that Harvey was in complete charge of the project for seventeen of the twenty-four months of construction, but during the first twelve of these months he all but brought his company to ruin. However, he should receive credit for recognizing the potential of the canal project and bringing it to the attention of Fairbanks in 1852, although his major promotional goal was entirely selfish.

Brooks too made his share of mistakes, and one of them was his failure to supervise Harvey closely at the upper cofferdam and the caisson gate. Nevertheless, the major credit for the fulfillment of the contract must go to Brooks. No other man in the service of the Canal Company could have driven the work so near to completion in 1854. Perhaps in recognition of this feat, Forbes finally made Brooks the president of the Michigan Central Railroad in 1855.

Corning's major contribution to the project (except for his own funds) was made at the very beginning. He seemed to have an almost uncanny knack for selecting as directors men who would be in the right spot with the right talent when they were needed. As a former governor and the brother of another, Fairbanks and Seymour could speak on equal terms with the Michigan officials, and Joy could deal skillfully with the legislators. Forbes could "lend" Brooks to the project because of his own interest in it. He and the Thayers also had access to the White House, as did Corning himself, though less directly, through Secretary of State Marcy. Seymour knew how to find labor recruiters in New York, and Fairbanks could produce landlookers from Maine. If Brooks had a wild financing plan, Pruyn could block it. Westerners and easterners balanced each other, and in the end the project met its deadline and achieved its goal.

From the moment the custody of the canal changed hands, the Canal Company had no further interest in it except for the minor finishing work to be completed under Harvey. The company's sole concern was for the lands granted. The canal itself would be placed in the charge of a succession of superintendents who were required to make annual reports to Lansing; the first of these was John Burt.

If Burt expected a rush of traffic following the opening of the canal, he was disappointed. Twenty-eight days passed after the opening before the *Illinois* reached the Sault again, this time with passengers and cargo for the Superior District. Next the steamer *Baltimore* ended its exile on Lake Superior. Business picked up but slowly during the rest of the year. As Greeley had written, the canal was essential, but the Upper Peninsula would need much more than that. There were piers to be erected, roads and rail roads to be built, and sandbars to be dredged. Above all, the area needed capital. At the close of the first navigation season, Burt reported that he had collected only $4,474.66 in tolls. Slightly over 109,000 tons had passed through the gates in the first year.[15]

As long as traffic was light, Burt could report the quantity of each item passing through the locks, thus giving a rough idea of life on Lake Superior. During the first season 1,217 barrels and boxes of liquor, ale, and beer traveled to Upper Michigan. In 1856, 2,173 barrels of liquor and 1,490 barrels of beer made the trip, along with 4 tombstones, 2 billiard tables, and 1 melodeon. Other goods brought in during 1856 included 17,686 barrels of flour, 3,551 barrels of beef, 4,316 barrels of pork, 4,296 boxes of candles, 3,968 tons of coal, and 3,323 bales of hay. Passengers totaled 4,674.[16]

There were many indications of progress in the mining industry of the Upper Peninsula. Eight steam engines, 12 steam boilers, and 26 pumps went up in 1856 to keep mines dry. The new copper mills required 42 stamps, and the rail road between the Jackson mine and Marquette obtained 62 cars in 1855 and 65 in 1856. In the second year of canal operation, more than 82,000 tons of machinery of all types were shipped in, along with 55 dozen shovels and 39 wagons. In the same year the shipment of more than 2,000 items of furniture, 158 individual doors, 76 bundles of doors, 220,000 shingles, 8 money safes, 36 dozen pails, more than 800 window sashes, and 886 boxes of glass gave evidence of increased permanent settlement. The Lake Superior district was not to be a farming area, however. Only 8 farm machines were brought up in the first two years of canal operation.[17]

The real justification for the canal would lie in the bulk material brought down from the Upper Peninsula. Burt estimated that the value of the down cargo was in excess of $2,800,000 in the first two years. Shipments amounted to 3,196 tons of copper in 1855 and

5,726 tons in 1856. The tonnage of iron ore jumped from 1,447 to 11,597 in one year. At the same time the tonnage of iron blooms (masses of wrought iron ready for further working) fell from 1,040 to 781 as the presence of the canal gradually doomed the tiny iron smelting industry of the Upper Peninsula. Bulk shipments of copper and iron increased steadily every year in the decade of 1850–60. Copper shipments totaled 5,759 tons in 1857, with the copper recorded as coming down from twenty-five different mines. In 1858 the total came to 6,944 tons, and in 1859 it was 7,245 tons. The figure jumped to above 9,000 tons in 1860, the pre-Civil War peak. (This was also the year canal superintendents abandoned the practice of itemizing individual items going west; superintendent Samuel Mead noted only that the people in the Upper Peninsula imported more than 9,000 barrels of beer in 1860.) In 1861 copper shipments fell to 7,645 tons, and in 1862 to 6,881 tons. Meanwhile, iron ore shipments from the Upper Peninsula continued to rise unevenly as shown in Table 2.[18]

TABLE 2

IRON ORE SHIPMENTS FROM THE
UPPER PENINSULA IN TONS, 1856–1862

1856	11,597
1857	26,184
1858	31,035
1859	65,769
1860	120,000
1861	44,836
1862	113,014

SOURCE: Reports of the canal superintendents for the years indicated.

State revenue from canal tolls increased every year except 1861 as a result not only of the increased tonnage going through the canal but also of an increase in tolls. The Canal Board raised these to 6¢ per ton in 1859 in order to retire new canal bonds. By 1860 the revenue reached $25,582, and superintendent George W. Brown urged that the tolls be reduced to 4¢ per ton. The day was long past when a superintendent like Burt would report as a major budget item the spending of $31.32 to buy oats for Lady Elgin, the canal mule.[19]

Each canal superintendent had to maintain the safety of the canal by guarding against structural weaknesses, weather hazards, and careless ship captains. In the first winter Burt adopted safety precautions that were usually followed by his successors. He kept the ditch filled with water, the lock gates closed, and the locks partially filled. He did not permit ice to accumulate at the lock gates because he feared that expansion would damage the gates.

Burt was troubled by the condition of the earth embankments at the cove just above the locks. In spite of precautions taken in the winter, he discovered that frost had penetrated to a depth of about six feet, and he feared that a sudden rise in the depth of Lake Superior during the spring thaw might cause a serious rupture between the frozen and unfrozen earth. Should a rise in the lake level occur at night, he would be helpless, for he could not work the caisson gate into place in the dark.[20]

As a solution for this problem, Burt suggested that a stone wall be constructed outside the embankments joining the upper lock wall to the solid rock excavation. He estimated that this would cost $20,000; if that was more than Michigan could afford, he suggested sheetpiling on the whole embankment. Burt's successor, Elisha Calkins, also recognized the danger but suggested that a wall of stone be erected inside the embankment with timber fender work along the top. Calkins thought that such a wall could be constructed during the winter so that the construction would not interfere with navigation. Apparently Calkins did not appreciate winter problems at the Sault; Harvey could have told him what happens to mortar if it is applied during a sharp frost. Pending instructions from Lansing, Calkins put his men to work reinforcing the embankments with earth. By this time the upper caisson gate had been demoted from "troublesome" to "perfect nuisance."[21]

Michigan authorities finally heeded the appeals of the canal superintendents and, in 1859, awarded a contract for the rebuilding of the earth walls to the firm of Holmes and Clark. Even this work did not prove adequate, and superintendent Samuel Mead added 10,000 cubic feet of earth as reinforcement in the summer of 1860. In the summer of 1861, Brown added more earth and stone and began the general improvement of the landscaping by planting trees. By 1862 the Holmes and Clark addition had begun to wash out, not from the water in the canal, but from the water in the river. The risk that Canfield had been forced to accept in 1852 when he made his

Fig. 5. Sidewheel passenger steamer *E. Ward*, of the Lake Superior Line leaving the locks. (An unknown hand has misidentified the ship as the *Baltimore*, which belonged to Sheldon McKnight and thus would not have been flying Eber Ward's pennant.) Reproduced from the collections of the Michigan Department of State, State Archives.

Fig. 6. The lock at the lower entrance in 1855. Reproduced from the collections of the Michigan Department of State, State Archives.

final decision on the course of the canal continued to haunt the Michigan authorities.[22]

In 1862 Brown was also casting nervous glances across the river, fearing British intervention in the Civil War. He urged state officials to ask that Fort Brady be repaired, armed, and manned by the United States Army. Fortunately, the measures did not prove to be necessary, but any eastern manufacturer depending upon Superior District sources of raw material would have a great concern for Anglo-American diplomatic relations. There are few structures as vulnerable as a canal in a war.[23]

Although Burt had to wait twenty-five days for the first ship to use the canal, the situation was soon reversed. Within four years an average of seven ships used the canal each day during July and August. Superintendent Mead reported new problems arising from the increased flow of traffic, problems that he correctly anticipated would grow in the future.[24]

A major concern was that ships waiting their turn in the locks needed more room to lay by. Ebenezer Warner's old dock, located in the St. Mary's River just south of the canal mouth, would have to go. To avoid the dock, ships had to anchor so far out in the river that they came under the influence of the rapids, a situation resulting in delay, confusion, and collisions. Further, when a ship under sail arrived running before a strong east wind, it would round Warner's dock so rapidly that checking lines could not be used, and the ship's captain would have the choice of ramming the canal pier or dropping anchor in the channel. Since the channel was both shallow and narrow at this point, dropping anchor was a dangerous option. Warner's dock lay within the limits of the canal right-of-way granted to Michigan, and Mead instituted legal proceedings for its removal. Eventually Warner came to terms and agreed to destroy his dock if the state would enlarge the anchorage basin.[25]

With the increased traffic, Canfield's design for the western end of the canal also came under criticism. To prevent the formation of a sandbar across the mouth of the canal, Canfield had ordered that the sand-catching pier be built in a curve. The underwater channel leading to the canal was therefore dredged in a curve to follow the pier line. Mead noted that there were several things wrong with this design. If the wind was unfavorable, a tug could tow only one schooner into the canal at a time (whereas if the channel had been straight, the tug could have pulled several in tandem). Further, if, under more favorable wind conditions, a captain tried to sail into the canal, it took a high degree of skill to keep from running into the curved pier. Finally, the current at this point was rapid enough to swing the sterns of schooners under tow into the bridge pier to the north. Mead wanted the arrangement at each end of the canal improved for safety and efficiency.[26]

There were other vexations of a minor nature. At intervals the sluice gates broke and allowed a strong current to enter the locks, making it necessary to apply extra force in opening the lock gates. Canfield's recommendation that a strong beacon be placed at the Lake Superior end had not been followed. At the urgent request of the ship captains, Mead furnished one in 1859. The sidewalls in the rock cutting had been cut at a slope of approximately thirty-two degrees for the purpose of maintaining strength in the banks, a feature steamboat captains found very annoying and at times dangerous. When steaming into the cut with a strong crosswind, they had difficulty staying clear of the downwind bank; and since the walls were jagged with many rock protrusions, there was a risk of underwater damage to the ships. The captains tried to avoid as much of the risk as possible by steaming rapidly through the cut to maintain headway. They therefore came into the area of the weak earth embankments at a speed higher than the legal limit, a practice that was hard on both the embankments and the superintendent's nerves. Mead asked that the sloping walls be replaced by perpendicular walls; he could then place wood fenders along the top of the canal to protect the ships.[27]

The Michigan authorities responded to the complaints of their superintendents only to the extent of authorizing the strengthening of the earth banks. The legislature in 1859 approved an issue of $100,000 of canal bonds. The state would guarantee payment of the interest and principal, but the money was expected to come from future canal revenue. Tolls were raised to 6¢ per ton, but what followed was something of a mystery. The bonds were sold, and presumably $100,000 passed into the hands of John McKinney, now the state treasurer. When it was discovered that half the sum was missing, McKinney was brought to trial. He was found guilty of embezzlement and spent most of the rest of his life in prison. He died without ever revealing the fate of the missing $50,000. The Canal

Board of Control used the rest of the fund to pay Holmes and Clark, but further improvements would have to wait. In the early 1860s Michigan and the United States had more important matters at hand.[28]

Eventually the steamship captains and owners complained of the inequity of charging the same canal toll for sailing ships and steamships. So much of the enrolled tonnage of the steamships was taken up in coal and machinery that they could not carry the payload of a schooner of similar enrolled tonnage. Superintendent Brown stated the case for the steamship people, using the *North Star* as an example. This steamship was enrolled at 1,106 tons, and thus her captain paid $66.36 every time she went through the locks. Because of the weight of her machinery and coal, she never carried more than 500 tons of cargo. A schooner of the same enrollment could carry much more freight and pay the same toll. In 1862 Brown noted that 543 schooners paid $1,100 less in tolls while carrying 45,000 tons more in freight than the steamers using the canal. He also noted that most of the steamships were owned by Michigan men, whereas most of the schooners were owned by out-of-state interests. Brown was obviously prejudiced in favor of the steamships. They were much easier to lock and could take care of themselves when the gates were opened. The sailing ships had to be manhandled through the locks, forcing Brown to bring his labor crew in from the embankment work. The argument between sail and steam continued until 1865, when the rate for steamers was lowered to 4½¢ per ton, and the sail rate remained at 6¢ per ton.[29]

As a general rule, the ship captains took great care not to damage the locks. No injuries to the gates were reported through 1862. There were plenty of arguments as to which ship had precedence at the locks, especially when two arrived at the same time, one from each direction. The superintendents had the authority to settle such arguments on the spot. They also took considerable pride in their canal. They ordered the gates, snubbing posts, and houses painted every other year, and each made his contribution to the cleaning up, landscaping, and fencing of the area. Despite the problems encountered during its first years of operation, the canal was proving itself a sound investment.[30]

11 The Canal Company Lands

Several questions arise regarding the Canal Company's acquisition of its lands. Without exception the men who actually inspected the lands had no financial interest in the company. In light of the knowledge available in the early 1850s, did these agents of the Canal Company select land wisely? Did the company then attempt to gain additional knowledge of the land selected, and, if so, how? Having gained possession of the 750,000 acres, what did the company eventually find on or under the land? Finally did the Canal Company make the best of what it had?

In order to answer these questions, it is necessary to consider the early history of mining activity in Michigan's Upper Peninsula. The white man had not waited for official settlement of the Indian title before entering the copper fields. In 1820 Lewis Cass referred to mining carried on by a few daring adventurers on the Eagle River near the Lake Superior coast. As miners and explorers pushed inland, they make a series of discoveries along the southwest branch of the Eagle River; and by 1848 the Boston and Pittsburgh Mining Company had opened two shafts of their Cliff Mine, discovered in 1845 in Township 58N, Range 32W, Section 36. This mine was one of the most successful in the early stages of Upper Peninsula mining; in 1851 the Cleveland *Daily Herald* called it "the marvel of the world." One mile southeast along the same river bank, the North American Company had opened its shaft in 1848 in Township 57N, Range 32W, Section 36. Other mines clustered in the general area. From that point prospectors worked their way south to the area near Portage Lake and today's town of Hancock. Here the Quincy mine was opened in 1847 in Township 55N, Range 34W, Section 26. The mineral wealth in the vicinity of Calumet, ten miles northeast of Hancock, was not discovered until 1864. Michigan geologist Douglass Houghton was quite aware of the copper deposits and had reported them to the legislature as early as 1841. He assumed that copper could be found in the greatest abundance along the plane of juncture of sedimentary rock and underlying trap rock; he also thought that it would take several years of hard work to prove out any mine. He was correct on both counts.[1]

The possible presence of copper received ample publicity. Greeley, who owned several shares in the Pennsylvania Mining Company, visited the Eagle River site in the summers of 1847 and 1848. He cited the Cliff Mine as being the most valuable, but he also warned of the risks involved in the copper fields, contending that the United States lease policy was a case of bad mismanagement of the mineral lands in the Upper Peninsula. *Hunt's Merchants' Magazine* added to Greeley's publicity. In April 1843 Freeman Hunt announced that Douglass Houghton had discovered a copper mass 98 percent pure and weighing between three and four tons. In 1844 Hunt recorded that a crew of twenty Cornish miners under the leadership of C. A. Gratiot was working at Eagle Harbor. By 1846 Hunt chided Greeley for his exaggerations but claimed that the area was valuable nonetheless. He wrote that the United States annually imported about 1,480 tons of copper at a price of 16¢ per pound and claimed that British copper mine owners had made a profit of $105,000 each year. Hunt also listed the names of twelve companies that, in 1846, were actively mining in the Upper Peninsula, and gave the approximate location of each mine.[2]

The publicity continued. In 1846 John R. St. John published his description of the Superior District, including the copper mining activity, but he also noted some of the same warnings that were to be advanced by Greeley. Days and weeks of labor must be spent without return. The men must be closely supervised by someone willing to go underground with them, and the business had its daily expenses regardless of the return or lack thereof. A year later Charles Lanman published his account of a canoe voyage he had made along the Lake Superior shore. He had no doubt about the value of the ore in the general area, but he wrote that an enormous amount of capital would be needed for successful operation, capital that most of the mine operators did not have. Lanman stated that he owned a few shares in a copper mining company, but he was "exceedingly anxious to dispose of my interests, at the earliest possible moment, on the most reasonable terms." He noted that everyone on Lake Superior had suddenly become an amateur geologist and that a good number of speculators had appeared in the vicinity.[3]

Yet even with all this publicity, it might have been difficult for a company about to claim a large quantity of land to obtain accurate information. To assure accurate and constant news from the mining area, John Ingersoll published his first edition of the *Lake Superior News and Miners' Journal* on 11 July 1846, at Copper Harbor. In 1851 Hunt again publicized mining activity, noting an increased shipment in the past year. He estimated that 1,100 tons of copper or copper ore had passed through the Sault from eight different mines. All this copper in 1851 had to be unloaded at the Lake Superior side, hauled across the portage on McKnight's rail road, and reloaded on the St. Mary's River.[4]

In addition to the obstacle at the Sault and the lack of capital, there were a number of reasons for the slow development of the copper fields. Copper was by no means in such demand as it would be after the inventions of Thomas Edison and Alexander Graham Bell in the 1870s and 1880s. Morse's telegraph, which had brought the news of Polk's nomination from Baltimore to Washington in 1844, consumed only a minor part of the copper production. With its high heat conductivity, copper was also used for kitchenware. Other uses included candlesticks, ornaments in churches, and sheathing for wooden ship hulls. In the 1850s, however, iron was in much greater demand, as was indicated by the yearly increases in iron ore shipped through the Sault Canal.

The government lease system also had done little to encourage exploitation, and Greeley's bitterness over the speculators' monopoly of the mineral lands was excessive. If the War Department figures were accurate, only 141 square miles of the Upper Peninsula were under government lease when the department suspended the leasing process, and more delays followed under the Treasury Department. It was this peculiar sequence of events, many months before the Canal Company was formed, that proved to be vital to the interests of the company. Only one further development was needed for the Canal Company to obtain valuable mineral land, and this took place at Sutter's Mill in 1848.

The story of what happened after the announcement of the

discovery of gold is well known, but it is impossible to determine completely the discovery's effect in the Midwest. However, it must have been substantial. Cyrus Woodman noted the repercussions in western Wisconsin, where the lead mining industry suffered between the spring of 1848 and the fall of 1853, and communities like Mineral Point lost numbers of their most vigorous citizens, who headed west to the diggings. It is reasonable to assume that the same thing happened in the Superior District. It is also reasonable to assume that venturesome easterners would choose California over the Ontonagon. Why endure the hardships of the Upper Peninsula, when with a little more effort one could go to California and pick up gold from the riverbeds? It was even possible that some of the War Department leaseholders selected California over their option to purchase land in Michigan. Woodman noted that the influence of the gold rush lasted until the fall of 1853. By that time the Canal Company was well into the process of land selection. No other possible sequence of events and policies could have placed the company in so favorable a position to obtain the best lands.[5]

To proceed successfully, however, the Canal Company needed specific and precise knowledge of the lands available. Rumor and gossip would not suffice in the copper area. For example, everyone knew that there was copper on the Keweenaw Peninsula, but there was no copper southwest of the Keweenaw fault plane. Knowledge of the precise location of the active mines was essential in order for the Canal Company to pick up all the adjacent unclaimed land, and on 10 April 1853 Harvey ordered Brown to obtain this information.[6]

If anything, Brown had more information available than he needed, thanks to both the United States and Michigan governments. He was no stranger in the area, and he could talk to miners and mineowners as they passed through the Sault. He probably had a complete file of Upper Peninsula newspapers dating back to the year when Ingersoll tried to publish at Copper Harbor. In addition he had available various government publications, especially those of the Thirty-first Congress published in 1849 and 1850. These congressional reports were especially valuable because they did much more than locate mines and mineral lands by some vague system of metes and bounds. References like Hunt's to "a copper mine on the Eagle River" were of little value, but the government surveyors and geologists located the mineral lands to the quarter section and sometimes to the quarter-quarter section, and these reports were available to anyone interested. For example, Congress had ordered that 10,000 copies be made of the report of J. W. Foster and J. D. Whitney, which not only included the exact location of copper mines but also listed the number of shafts sunk and the number of men employed.[7]

Brown also had access to the report of United States geologist Charles Jackson. The result of a survey made in 1847 and 1848, it included a geological map of the Upper Peninsula land between Portage Lake and the Montreal River as well as a four-page list of copper lands and detailed locations down to quarter sections. Jackson even indicated the sites, like Copper Harbor, where claims should not be made because mining activity had stopped. In addition there was another report by J. W. Foster and S. W. Hill that listed mine locations and stated the average monthly pay for mine workers.[8]

Finally, Brown could consult a State of Michigan reference published in 1850, the report of Stephen V. R. Trowbridge, assistant agent of United States mineral lands. Besides including an excellent description of mining under primitive conditions, Trowbridge gave the location of mines in operation, listed the ones that had actually made shipments, and noted the one mining company (Pittsburgh and Boston Cliff) that had already paid a stock dividend. Trowbridge also reported that the Jackson Iron Company was in operation, having shipped fifty tons of blooms in 1849, and that the Marquette Iron Company was about to begin operations.[9]

Precision was not as important in claiming iron ore locations as in claiming the copper sites farther west. If one section contained high-grade iron ore, there was a good chance that the surrounding sections did so as well. Harvey could safely order Brown to claim everything available in a three-mile strip around the Jackson and Marquette sites, plus a block of about five thousand acres at the mouth of the Chocolay River, particularly since federal sources available included a map of the iron fields with fifty-two ore locations listed by the quarter-quarter section.[10]

In spite of his own wide experience plus all the printed material available, Brown took one further step to assure that the Canal Company would get the best mineral land available. In the spring of 1853, he hired J. D. Whitney as a mineral landlooker for the summer. This was Brown's greatest service to the Canal Company, and of course it was provided several months before the outbreak of the dispute with Harvey. Since Whitney had already made a geological survey, he would need to do little more than review the results of his previous work in the light of any new discoveries made in the interval. Brown paid Whitney $500, a handsome sum for a few months' work, but the information gained was well worth the expense, since it resulted in Canal Company ownership, at least for a time, of potentially valuable mineral land.[11]

The Canal Company's policy toward the acquisition of pineland was stated by Brooks in simple terms in 1854: "There is more pine in the state that we can take but we of course try to get that of such a grade that there may be little or none left as good as that we take." For a number of reasons, Brooks's goal was difficult to achieve. Governor Parsons had commissioned Harvey as a state agent to select land for the company in April 1853. He also commissioned George Frost on 10 June and Deodatus Whitwood on 8 July of the same year. These three men were too few for such a large undertaking, and two of them carried, or tried to carry, heavy responsibilities in connection with the actual building of the canal as well. The Canal Company could only be assured of obtaining high-quality timberland by sending someone out to look at the land and make an expert judgment on the spot—and therein lay the problem. Landlookers hired by the company would have to be completely reliable, because none of the Canal Company officers would have the time to inspect their findings. It would be a simple matter for an unscrupulous or lazy landlooker to disappear behind the first hill with his supplies and a jug, merely to camp out, loaf, and fish for several weeks and then return to submit a fictitious report.[12]

Another problem was the necessity to cover an enormous amount of land, either on foot or in a canoe. A canoeing landlooker could more easily inspect a broader area, but he would have to be careful in forming conclusions. He might see a magnificent stand of timber on both banks, but one hundred yards inland the timber might peter out into poor farmland. There would be vast acreages burned out, and these must be located and avoided. Today, one man with a camera and an airplane could do the job in a few days; in the 1850s it was not so simple.

In the first year of exploration, with Harvey in charge, the landlooking process fell as far behind schedule as progress on the canal itself. Once again, Harvey proved that he did not understand the magnitude of the task set before him. In the first place, he did not have two full years to conduct a land search. Little could be done in the winter months, when many parts of Michigan were inaccessible. Then, toward the end of the process, time must be reserved for handling all the paperwork and for winning approval in Washington. Brooks began to worry about the situation as early as June 1853, fearing that the Canal Company would lose the best of the mineral lands. As usual, Harvey was completely confident and wrote that he was quite satisfied with Brown's work. Nevertheless, by September 1853 the Canal Company had reserved only about 277,000 acres, much less than half the total allocated. Harvey had reserved 27,000 acres in the Upper Peninsula, the bulk being described as mineral lands, and Frost had set aside about 250,000 acres of pineland in the Lower Peninsula. The two men had only six search parties in the field, and Harvey wrote that he would reserve only a total of 77,000 acres in the Superior District.[13]

Brooks redoubled the effort when he assumed full responsibility for land selection in 1854, but even when Fairbanks sent him lumbermen from Maine to help, he was not completely satisfied. He noted that the Maine men insisted on carrying more equipment into the field than western men usually took, a practice that delayed their progress. He was also forced to relocate some of the land reserved in the previous year when it turned out to be of little value. Nevertheless, by 27 March 1854 Brooks had eighteen search parties in the field and expected that Whitwood would send out still more from Detroit. The reliability problem was partially solved by sending men into the field in parties of three, and by the end of the summer there were seventy-five landlookers at work. Brooks even employed government surveyors as landlookers, but this practice proved to be an inconvenience when the surveyors were called back into government service in the late spring of 1854, and Brooks had to regroup his teams. Brooks also asked Fairbanks to return one of the most valuable Maine men for a second summer of work to "re-look" the lands. It was a wise decision. In later years the Canal Company would claim that the selections had been made as the result of investigations made by two separate parties. A negative report from either would be a cause for rejection. The company also claimed that each forty- or eighty-acre lot had been individually inspected. Considering the enormous number of quarter-quarter sections selected, this claim was an exaggeration, but Brooks did make the effort to check the selections made in 1853.[14]

When the looking task was over, Frost had the job of preparing to file the company's claims—an enormous problem in bookkeeping. In the Lower Peninsula the Canal Company claimed over 212,000 acres in the Cheboygan Land District in the north, as well as almost 227,000 acres in the eastern Genessee District. The balance of the Lower Peninsula land was claimed through the Detroit office. Finally, the company claimed almost 253,000 acres in the Upper Peninsula through the Superior District office at Sault Ste. Marie. It was important that Frost not claim land already owned by others, since costly litigation could result. With such a high total acreage claimed, however, it was almost inevitable that slips of this nature would occur. The complaints began to come in as early as May 1855.[15]

Frost had other pitfalls to avoid, such as the error of claiming the same piece of land twice. There was a danger that in one entry he might claim a quarter-quarter section, and many entries later he might inadvertently claim a half-quarter that would include the first forty acres. In all the 1,422 separate entries in the Upper Peninsula, Frost never made that error. His task was further complicated by the fact that he was not permitted to claim an entire section, "except for the northeast quarter of the northwest quarter." If the Canal Company wanted to claim an entire section except for a quarter-quarter, as it sometimes did, Frost would have to prepare four separate entries for the one section. In the end Frost's accounting was almost impeccable, considering that he had to make allowances for deletions, additions, and surveying adjustments. He thought that he had claimed 252,966.27 acres in the Upper Peninsula, when actually he had claimed 252,958.10, an error of only about 8 acres.[16]

The Canal Company eventually classified about half the total claim, or 373,000 acres, as good, accessible timberland. It anticipated that 190,000 acres would prove to be mineral land, and it left the remaining 187,000 acres unclassified. It must be assumed that the latter consisted of farmlands or relatively inaccessible timberlands. As will be seen, the mineral total was too high, which meant that the Canal Company owned additional acres of timber in the Upper Peninsula.[17]

The largest single timber claim made by the company was in the area of the Saginaw River in the Lower Peninsula. Advertising the ease with which the timber could be extracted by water, the company claimed 100,000 acres along this route. It also claimed 61,000 acres of timber along the Muskegon River, 56,000 acres along the Manistee, 42,000 acres along the Pere Marquette, and 21,000 acres along the White River. Finally, the company claimed 59,000 acres of timber at Thunder Bay.[18]

On the Keweenaw Peninsula in Upper Michigan, where the Canal Company hoped to own copper land, Brown and his employee J. D. Whitney had varied luck. With several important exceptions they claimed land next to areas where copper had already been reported, and in many cases they were able to obtain the reported land. As a general rule, the line of claims followed along the approximate location of the Keweenaw fault plane. Any land claimed to the southeast of this plane would be of little value, since it would not contain copper; and its timber, if any, would be difficult to extract. The only major area so claimed was a solid block of over 8,000 acres lying between Portage Lake and the fault plane.[19]

Either Brown or Whitney established the policy of claiming whatever land was available along the line of the fault plane even if no copper had been reported in that particular area. Under this policy the Canal Company claimed a great deal of worthless land, but it also claimed some of the best. For example, the government authorities had not reported copper along the fault plane between the site of the present towns of Winona on the southwest and Houghton on the northeast. For the southern two-thirds of the line, the authorities proved to be correct, and the Canal Company gained ownership of land of little value. Not only did it lack copper, but also any timber along this line would be most difficult to extract. However, in the northeast third of the line, below Houghton, the policy paid off. Although the government men had not reported copper in the area, the company gained possession of quite valuable land, including all the land that would eventually be worked by the Champion Mining Company (219,201 tons; $29,070,261), approximately two-thirds of the land of the future Baltic Mining Company (131,761 tons; $10,001,772), and about half the land from which the Atlantic Mining Company would extract copper (59,141 tons; $990,000).[20]

In the same area below Houghton, the Canal Company narrowly

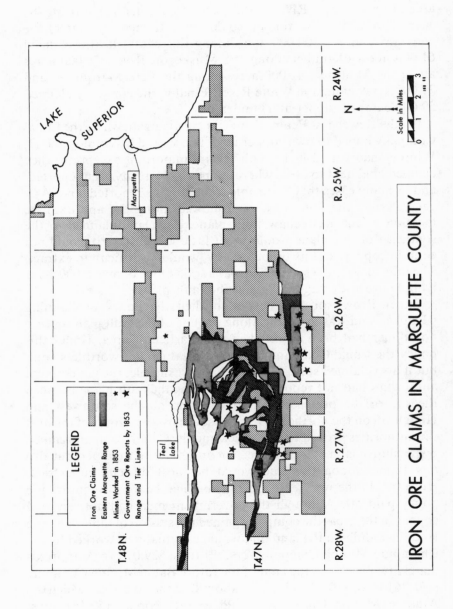

LAKE SUPERIOR

Marquette

Teal Lake

LEGEND

Iron Ore Claims

Eastern Marquette Range

Mines Worked in 1853 ⋆

Government Ore Reports by 1853 ★

Range and Tier Lines

T.48N.

T.47N.

R.28W.   R.27W.   R.26W.   R.25W.   R.24W.

N

Scale in Miles

0   1   2   3

IRON ORE CLAIMS IN MARQUETTE COUNTY

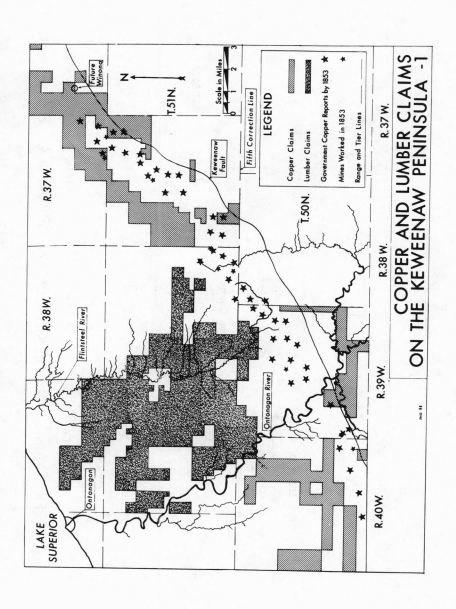

COPPER AND LUMBER CLAIMS
ON THE KEWEENAW PENINSULA -1

LEGEND

| | Copper Claims |
| | Lumber Claims |
★ Government Copper Reports by 1853
★ Mines Worked in 1853
— Range and Tier Lines

Scale in Miles
0 1 2 3

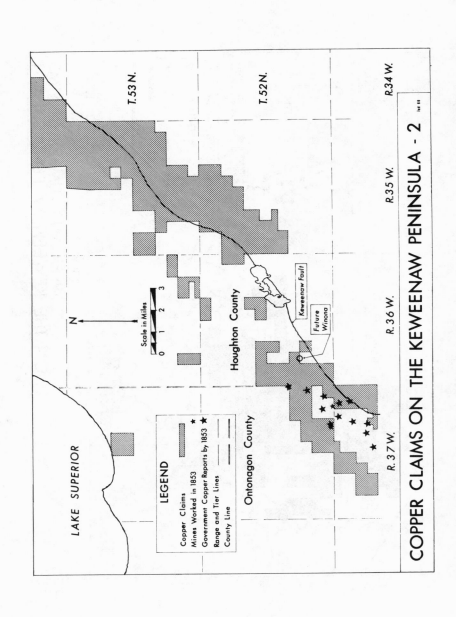

LEGEND

Copper Claims

Mines Worked in 1853 ★

Government Copper Reports by 1853 ★

Range and Tier Lines

County Line

LAKE SUPERIOR

Ontonagon County

Houghton County

T. 53 N.

T. 52 N.

R. 37 W.

R. 36 W.

R. 35 W.

R. 34 W.

N

Scale in Miles

0   1   2   3

Keweenaw Fault

Future Winona

COPPER CLAIMS ON THE KEWEENAW PENINSULA - 2

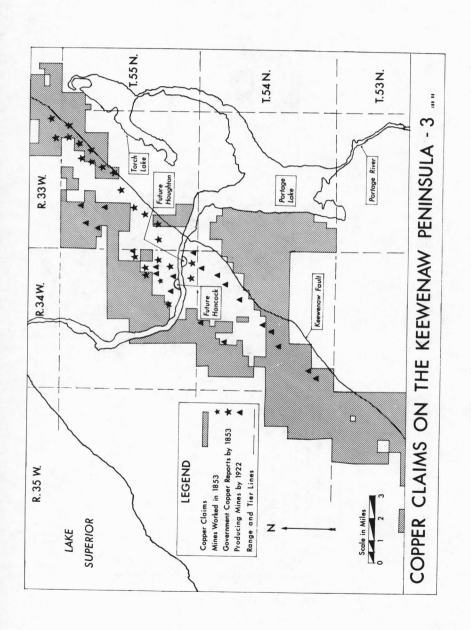

COPPER CLAIMS ON THE KEEWENAW PENINSULA - 3

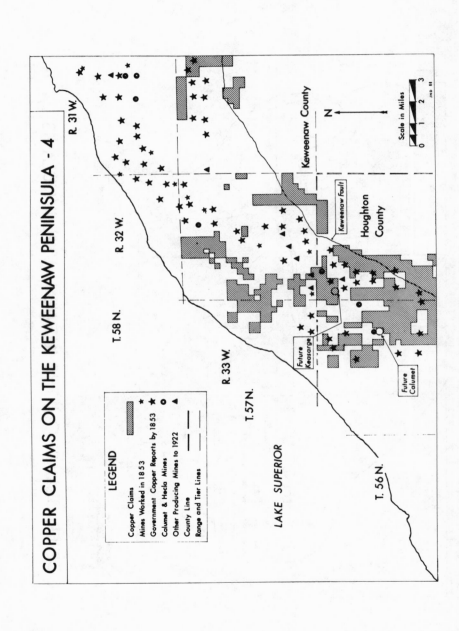

COPPER CLAIMS ON THE KEWEENAW PENINSULA - 4

LEGEND

▨	Copper Claims
★	Mines Worked in 1853
★	Government Copper Reports by 1853
◉	Calumet & Hecla Mines
▲	Other Producing Mines to 1922
——	County Line
- - -	Range and Tier Lines

R. 31 W.

R. 32 W.

R. 33 W.

T. 58 N.

T. 57 N.

T. 56 N.

Keweenaw County

Houghton County

Keweenaw Fault

Future Keasarge

Future Calumet

LAKE SUPERIOR

N

Scale in Miles

0 1 2 3

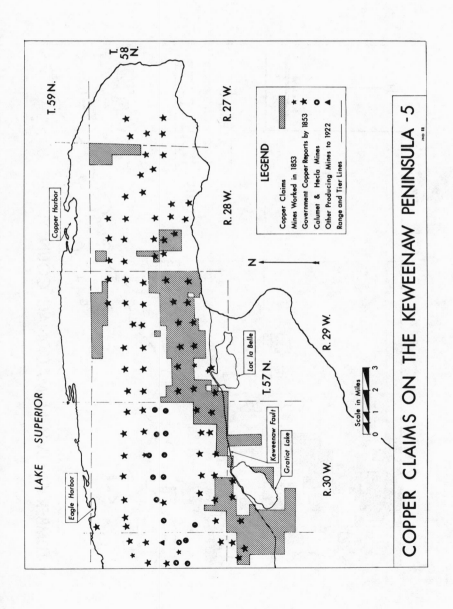

COPPER CLAIMS ON THE KEWEENAW PENINSULA - 5

LEGEND

- Copper Claims
- ★ Mines Worked in 1853
- ★ Government Copper Reports by 1853
- ○ Calumet & Hecla Mines
- ▲ Other Producing Mines to 1922
- — Range and Tier Lines

LAKE SUPERIOR

Eagle Harbor

Copper Harbor

T. 59 N.

T. 58 N.

T. 57 N.

R. 27 W.

R. 28 W.

R. 29 W.

R. 30 W.

Lac la Belle

Keweenaw Fault

Gratiot Lake

N

Scale in Miles
0 1 2 3

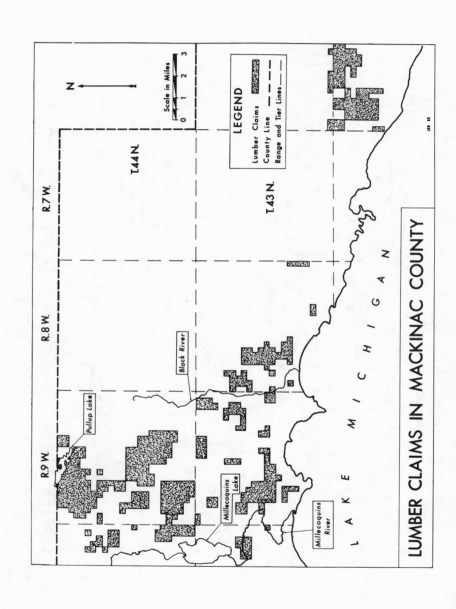

LUMBER CLAIMS IN MACKINAC COUNTY

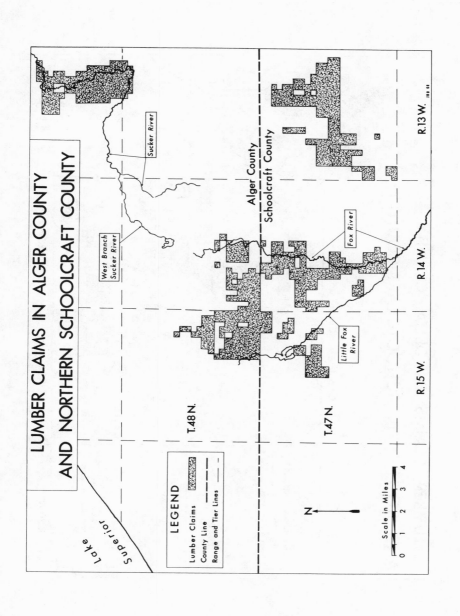

LUMBER CLAIMS IN ALGER COUNTY
AND NORTHERN SCHOOLCRAFT COUNTY

Lake Superior

Sucker River

West Branch Sucker River

Alger County

Schoolcraft County

Fox River

Little Fox River

LEGEND

Lumber Claims

County Line

Range and Tier Lines

T.48 N.

T.47 N.

R.15 W.

R.14 W.

R.13 W.

N

Scale in Miles

0   1   2   3   4

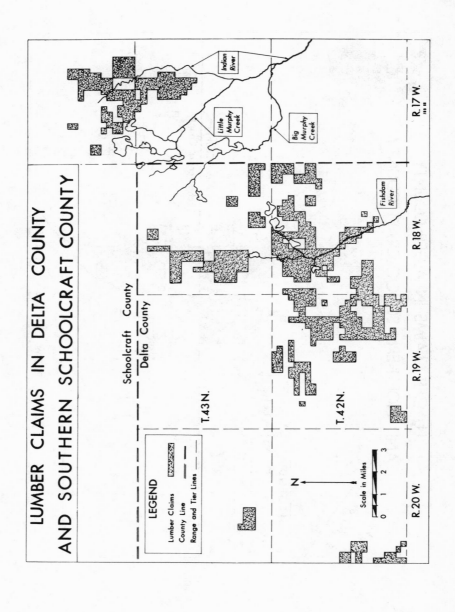

LUMBER CLAIMS IN DELTA COUNTY
AND SOUTHERN SCHOOLCRAFT COUNTY

LEGEND

Lumber Claims
County Line
Range and Tier Lines

Schoolcraft County
Delta County

T. 43 N.

T. 42 N.

R. 20 W.

R. 19 W.

R. 18 W.

R. 17 W.

Indian River

Little Murphy Creek

Big Murphy Creek

Fishdam River

N

Scale in Miles

0   1   2   3

missed owning more valuable land. It completely surrounded a series of claims made by others, but to no avail. In between lay the lands that would eventually yield copper for the Isle Royale Mining Company (90,286 tons; $2,550,000). In several places the Canal Company claims ran to within a few hundred yards of Isle Royale property. The same situation existed immediately north of Hancock. Here the government had indicated the presence of copper, but it must be assumed that the best lands had been claimed before 1853. The Canal Company lands all but surrounded the land that would yield wealth for the Quincy Mining Company (363,011 tons; $27,002,508).[21]

Four and a half miles northeast of Hancock, the Canal Company ran into better luck. Once again claiming land that the government agents had neglected, the company gained all the acreage that would eventually produce copper for the Franklin Mining Company (77,158 tons; $1,240,000). The Canal Company did not do so well, however, with about 6,400 acres it took northwest of Torch Lake. Although government agents had proclaimed the presence of copper there, the land proved to be of little value. The best claims of all were made in Township 55N, Range 33W, just south of the present town of Calumet. The company claimed all but 120 acres of Section 23, and it was on this land that the first great Calumet lode was discovered and mined. The company also claimed 420 acres of Section 26 immediately to the south; the Hecla Mining Company would exploit this land. Finally, the company claimed land in three other sections in the township to the west, around the present town of Kearsarge, and this land formed the base when the two operations merged in 1871 to create the Calumet and Hecla Company (1,621,008 tons; $148,413,051). Their combined holdings included 2,480 acres that once had belonged to the Canal Company. The government had indicated the presence of copper on only 220 acres of this land.[22]

The Canal Company made only one other valuable mineral claim on the Keweenaw Peninsula. Following the fault plane further northeast, it gained possession of 120 acres that would become about one-third of the mineral land holdings of the Allouez Mining Company (54,604 tons; $2,850,000). Although the Canal Company claimed land beyond the Allouez location to within three and a half miles of the tip of the peninsula, it gained little of value there. In claiming over 11,000 acres, it missed what would become Calumet and Hecla property by two miles. It claimed Mt. Horace Greeley and a solid block of land north of Lac la Belle to no avail. Through some perverse stroke of luck, the company found its best land when it ignored the reports of government surveyors and took claims on the northwest side of the fault plane.[23]

The Canal Company also claimed over 27,000 acres of timberland on the Keweenaw Peninsula southeast of Ontonagon. Timber could be removed from the area on either the Ontonagon River on the west or the Flintsteel River on the east. This claim, together with the fault plane claims, encompassed a considerable area and all but cut the Keweenaw Peninsula in two. It would be possible for a man landing at Ontonagon from Lake Superior to reach Canal Company land by walking southeast for half a mile. Continuing in this direction thirteen miles, he would arrive at the area of the fault plane. A change in direction to the northeast would take him out on the Keweenaw Peninsula, and by walking a relatively straight line for fifty-five miles he would arrive back on Lake Superior in Allouez Township. During this entire trip of sixty-nine miles, he would have walked on Canal Company lands for all but six miles, and he would not have been off company lands for more than a mile at a time. Under the circumstances, the company's reputation for creating a land monopoly in the area was hardly surprising.[24]

The experience of the Canal Company in the copper fields was reversed in the iron fields west of Marquette. In this area there were far fewer government reports to work with, but these turned out to be more accurate than the reports in the copper fields. When Brown and Whitney made their selections according to these reports, they picked up some highly valuable iron ore land. When they deviated, the land selected contained little of mineral value. From their ability to cluster their claims, it was obvious that competition had not arrived as it had in the copper fields. In fact, in 1853 there were only two iron ore mines in operation west of Marquette.[25]

For some reason Brown and Whitney decided to ignore Harvey's instructions to claim 5,000 acres at the mouth of the Chocolay River. Apparently there was no valuable timber on the spot, and the location was over eight miles from the iron fields. They did claim 920 acres, including the site for the future town of Harvey. From the Harvey location the Canal Company claimed land in a nearly complete semicircle around Marquette. There were no minerals to be found in this claim of about 11,000 acres.[26]

The principal location of the eastern part of the Marquette iron range lay in two townships, 47N, and Ranges 26W and 27W. Here the Canal Company made its best claims, taking more than one-third of the available land, or almost 19,000 acres. The company did not, however, try to establish claims in the three minor ore enclaves to the west located near today's towns of Republic, Humboldt, and Michigamme, although iron had been reported there. It was difficult enough in 1853 to haul ore from the Jackson mine south of Teal Lake to Marquette. Humboldt, the nearest to Marquette of the three enclaves, was twice as far away. The opening of these areas would have to wait a few more years, and in any case the locations south of Nagaunee and Ishpeming would furnish more than an adequate supply of iron ore for the time being. By the end of 1862, 435,625 tons had been extracted and hauled through the Sault locks.[27]

The Canal Company claimed additional timberland in the Upper Peninsula. By exploring the river and lake network of eastern Delta County, it located over 17,000 acres of timber that could be brought to market via the tributaries of the Sturgeon and Fishdam Rivers, since both empty into Big Bay de Noc on Lake Michigan. The serrated edges of many of the claims indicate that the inspection was quite selective. The largest single block of land claimed in the district was only 2,240 acres.[28]

The company landlookers also discovered 20,000 acres of timber in the eastern part of Alger County and the northern part of Schoolcraft County. These lands were located on or near the Sucker River, which empties into Lake Superior at Grand Marais, and on the branches of the Fox River, which empties via the Manistique River into Lake Michigan. Again the process was selective, since the largest single block claimed was only 3,200 acres along the east branch of the Fox River. Less wisely selected was a block of 5,100 acres near Pull Up Lake in the western part of Mackinac County, from which it would be most difficult to extract timber because the center of the area was eight miles north of Lake Michigan, and there were no rivers available. Here land had been selected that would prove difficult to sell, a mistake that the company seldom made in the Upper Peninsula.[29]

The remainder of the Superior District timber claims were small and scattered. The Canal Company claimed nothing in Menominee, Dickinson, Gogebic, or Iron counties, not knowing of the existence of the Menominee iron range. It claimed only minor acreages in the Chippewa, Luce, and Baraga counties.

In a few instances the Canal Company claimed areas, some quite small, because of immediate necessity or anticipated future growth. In the former case it claimed several lots on Hay Lake to assure access to Section 16, from which Harvey took timber for the canal. Examples of the latter situation are more numerous. The semicircle around Marquette represented a speculation upon the growth of the community, since anyone wanting to haul iron ore to the crude dock at Marquette would have to pass through Canal Company lands. The company claimed a similar semicircle around the little village of Baraga on Keweenaw Bay. It also selected lands at the mouth of the Portage River near the present location of a United States Coast Guard station, perhaps anticipating that the Portage River would some day be part of a canal cutting through the Keweenaw Peninsula.[30]

Although Brown had predicted that Sault Ste. Marie would become another Detroit once the canal was completed, the Canal Company officers did not accept this prediction; and, with the exception of the strategically located lots on Hay Lake, the company did not claim an inch of land within fifty miles of the canal. This judgment proved sound, and the lands selected by the company were, by and large, wisely chosen. Thus the company officers and stockholders had been well compensated for the construction of the canal. It would now be up to them to make the best of their land.

12 Land for Sale

In theory the officers of the Canal Company had two options. First, they could attempt to exploit their lands by forming the appropriate subsidiary companies for copper mining, iron mining, and lumbering. This option, which would have required a fresh infusion of capital, was never seriously considered. When Harvey suggested that the company float a $50,000 bond issue, Pruyn rejected the idea out of hand. Many railroad men like Brooks and Joy were, for good reason, chronically overextended. As the railroad frontier moved westward, the owners of the eastern trunk lines believed that the taking of new risks was essential to survival. They had large fixed indebtedness, and, should the new western roads divert traffic to competing lines, the results might be unfortunate. Thus, in the years before 1875, Brooks and Joy attempted with considerable success to gain control over roads like the Chicago, Burlington, and Quincy. The resulting overextension was at times professional and physical as well as financial, and it is not surprising that, with the exception of coal mining, the railroad men were not willing to launch mining ventures. In fact, it was just as well that they did not try: in the two decades after 1845, a total of ninety-four Superior District copper companies made capital calls on their stockholders of more than $13,100,000; during this same period the companies declared dividends of only $5,600,000.[1]

The other option was to sell the lands at the best price possible, a choice that met with Brooks's enthusiastic approval. Brooks had once tried to interest Fairbanks in financing a railroad to the Mackinac Straits in order to increase the value of the company's timberlands. Now, in the summer of 1855, he wrote to Corning no fewer than six times urging prompt disposal of the company's mineral lands. At first Brooks was under the impression that each stockholder of the Canal Company would receive a share of the lands for personal use. He and Joy believed that the mineral lands were worth well over $1,000,000, and Brooks offered to sell his share to either Corning or Fairbanks, whichever would pay the most. However, Corning and Fairbanks were in no hurry to sell the lands, although Corning considered the idea of sending Elon Farnsworth, a former state officer of Michigan who had already helped the Canal Company solve several minor problems, to London to try to find a market. Meanwhile, Brooks would have to be patient.[2]

For the time being, the company directors decided to operate with two land offices for the management and sale of timberlands. George Frost supervised the undertaking from his office in Detroit, and Harvey opened a second office at Marquette. As to the mineral lands, Frost sent Corning a bundle of maps locating Canal Company lands for the use of Farnsworth. The officers still were not satisfied with the quality of information available regarding the mineral lands, and Fairbanks wanted a more complete exploration made; but Corning decided to attempt to sell the lands even without adequate knowledge of their wealth. In the fall of 1855, he went to Europe to look for a British market, and Brooks ordered Harvey to stop the sale of mineral lands pending the outcome of the trip. However, Corning was not able to find a buyer. With the Crimean War in progress, the British specie supply was tight, and London investors could get good rates in their own markets and in fact were getting ready to call in their own loans from the United States.[3]

Meanwhile, conflicting news came down from the Superior District. Harvey sent Fairbanks a depressing report about the prospects in the copper fields, but on the very same day he gave a much more optimistic report to Seymour. In this he noted that a valuable copper discovery had been made near Portage Lake, and that the Canal Company owned the adjoining sections of land. He suggested that a considerable cash outlay would be justified to prove the presence of copper on the company land. Harvey was correct up to a point. The copper discovery in 1855 was indeed valuable and eventually became the property of the Quincy Mining Company (363,001 tons; $27,002,500). However, there was no copper on the adjacent lands of the Canal Company.[4]

Harvey did manage to sell some of the non-mineral lands that he described as being suitable for agriculture. He told Fairbanks that he had sold 680 acres in 1855 at prices that ranged from $5 to $12 per acre. However, he admitted that he had concluded a number of verbal deals, accepting down payments and notes, since he did not have proper facilities and forms. This was an excellent way of ensuring future trouble. As to the sale of mineral lands, Harvey did not expect that Corning would be successful in Europe. When released from his orders to sell mineral land, he announced that he was getting ready to hire printers and to advertise.[5]

In fact, so slowly did the sale of land proceed that all the Canal Company officers had been dead for many years when the last of the Michigan holdings were disposed of, although men like Corning and Fairbanks lived long enough to reap a substantial, if not exorbitant, reward for the risks of 1853–55. In 1858 the company's officers adopted a plan devised by Harvey to separate the management and sale of the mineral lands from that of the pinelands in the Lower Peninsula; they formed the Saint Mary's Canal Mineral Land Company,[6] with Erastus Fairbanks as president. No cash changed hands, but in return for 180,991.22 acres in the Upper Peninsula, the Canal Company received 15,000 shares of the stock of the Mineral Company. These 15,000 shares constituted only a quarter of the total stock issue, and the remaining shares were taken up by the officers of the Canal Company. In 1860 the same men traded 1,625 acres to the Albany and Boston Mining Company in return for 10,000 shares of the Albany and Boston stock. Each shareholder in the Mineral Company received one share of Albany and Boston stock for each four shares of Mineral Company stock held. The exchange turned out to be a dubious venture. The Albany and Boston Company operated for only ten years and never paid a dividend. Its maximum production, in 1865, amounted to only 159 tons of copper. In the 1880s the property was sold to other interests.[7]

Twenty-five years after the death of Corning, the Mineral Company still owned lands in the Upper Peninsula. In 1897 the Baltic Mining Company organized and purchased land in Houghton County from the Mineral Company. By 1925 the Baltic Company had paid over $10,000,000 in dividends. In 1899, in what was perhaps the most successful single transaction made by Corning's successors, the Mineral Company traded more of its land

to the Champion Mining Company in return for half of the
Champion's stock. The Champion Company commenced
operations in 1902 and was successful for the next twenty-two years.
During the period it paid dividends of over $29,000,000, of which
half went to the stockholders of the Mineral Company. In 1931 the
Copper Range Consolidated Company absorbed both the Champion Mining Company and the Mineral Company.[8]

Despite its success, the Mineral Company sold some of its land
too soon. During the Civil War it sold to the Iron Cliffs Company
about 38,000 of its 41,508 acres in Marquette County for a reported
purchase price of $500,000, a fraction of the eventual value of the
iron ore on the land. Again, in 1865, the Mineral Company sold 160
acres to the Calumet Mining Company for $60,000. It was later
estimated that the mine located on this quarter section was worth
$13,000,000. It should be noted, however, that because of the crude
state of mining technology it took the extraordinary efforts of
Alexander Agassiz to put the Calumet and Hecla on a paying basis.
The energetic son of Louis Agassiz traded his health for the copper
wealth of Upper Michigan. In the winter of 1867, he wrote a letter
that echoed the ones Brooks had written over a decade before: "It is
fortunate that I am tough, for if I were not I should have broken
down; but I begin to feel the effect of this infernal work and drive; I
get fearfully tired." Perhaps Brooks could have managed the same
feat to the great enrichment of the Mineral Company, but he was too
busy with railroad affairs to consider it.[9]

The original owners of the Mineral Company were unfortunate in
that they obtained their copper lands at the wrong moment in the
history of American technology. Alexander Agassiz faced a
declining market and increased foreign competition even as he
toiled in the Upper Peninsula. Iron ships did not require copper
sheathing as did wooden ships, and the decision of the government
to begin a steel war fleet in the administration of Chester Arthur was
of no help to the copper industry. Nor were Thomas Edison and
Alexander Graham Bell, who were barely out of their teens and still
years away from creating a world demand for copper.[10]

The pineland holdings of the Canal Company were also difficult
to sell or manage. In 1857 Frost published a catalogue of the
holdings, with lumber statistics and maps. The company offered
timberland at prices that ranged from $5 to $15 per acre, depending

upon the quality and quantity of the timber. One-fifth of the payment was required at the time of purchase, with the balance due in four yearly installments at an interest rate of 6 percent per year. Other land located on rivers (probably farmland) was available at between $5 and $8 per acre. The following year the company published a directors report that included most of the information offered in the catalogue the year before. The trouble was that 1857 and 1858 were not good years in which to sell land. A combination of factors, including the withdrawal of British investments in the United States and excessive speculation in land and railroads, brought about panic and depression—and then came the Civil War.[11]

A company stockholder, questioning Forbes about the prospect of the sale of land, concluded, "As for the Sault Ste. Marie the pine lands must wait for the prairie farmers to build again." However, the directors could not wait for the end of the war. In May 1860 the tax-exempt status of the land expired, and the state of Michigan began to tax at once. Two years later the cost of administration and taxes for the Canal Company's lands was estimated at $50,000 a year. Therefore, in the spring of 1862, the company launched a major effort to sell the 100,000-acre tract along the Saginaw River. To handle the sale, twelve agencies were established in Detroit, Boston, Chicago, Springfield, Albany, Buffalo, New York, and other places, including St. Johnsbury, where Fairbanks would try to sell land.[12]

Prominent among the new agents was Cyrus Woodman, whose reputation as a western land agent was well established by 1862. In 1847 he had been selected as the Wisconsin Territory's representative on the River and Harbor executive committee, and before that he had served as the western land agent for the Boston and Western Land Company, a difficult and exasperating job that did little to enhance his local popularity. He was, in the first place, responsible for the holdings of absentee landowners. He had to see that the lands were protected from trespassers and timber poachers. Taxes must be paid promptly. He had to make the best possible bargain when selling land because his sole income came from commissions. If a sale had been made on a credit basis, he was responsible for the collection of the balance plus the interest, a difficult duty to perform in a depression. When Woodman accepted the agent's position for the Canal Company, he moved to Detroit, where he lived for the next two years.[13]

The directors set the minimum price on the Saginaw River land at $3 per acre. The terms were one-quarter cash, with the balance due in three yearly payments at 7 percent interest per year. In spite of the efforts of Woodman and his associates, the sale was a failure. Buyers took only 10,000 acres, and of this land less than 40 percent was paid for. The problem was twofold. First, in the same months that the company advertised its great sale, the Homestead Act went into effect with Lincoln's signature, and Michigan was not in the best geographical position to furnish lumber where it was now most needed, in the trans-Mississippi west; it cost enough to ship lumber west from Wisconsin and Minnesota. Second, there was little demand for Michigan farmlands. With the rural lads flocking to the Army of the Tennessee, the remaining farmers were hard pressed to handle the land already under cultivation.[14]

The failure of the sale brought about the first major disagreement among the directors of the Canal Company. Corning and Fairbanks wanted to divide the pine holdings among the stockholders, so that each could assume responsibility for the management and sale of his own plots. The Boston-based directors and chief stockholders, on the other hand, were reluctant to accept a division and personal responsibility. This group included Forbes, Nathaniel Thayer, J. N. Denison, J. N. A. Griswold, and Brooks, who by 1862 was established in Boston as president of the Michigan Central Railroad. In the end each side had its way. The Boston men agreed to a division if an equitable formula could be found but planned to form their own association after the division had been accomplished.[15]

Fortunately for all concerned, Woodman was available to carry out the task. He had performed exactly the same service for the Boston and Western Land Company in 1840 to the satisfaction of the owners. Now, in 1863, he proceeded to divide the pine holdings of the Canal Company into 747 parcels of varying size and value. He then published a catalogue in which he described the land parcels, estimated the value of each, and announced the terms of sale. At the auction stockholders of the Canal Company would be permitted to pay for up to 90 percent of their land with company stock. The balance was to be paid in cash or Canal Company bonds. The general public could purchase on terms of 50 percent down, with the balance due in one year at 7 percent interest. Payments by the public were to be in cash or Canal Company bonds. Woodman scheduled the auction for 2 September 1863 in Detroit.[16]

The event was a success. According to Woodman's calculations, land valued at $900,000 was sold, with the majority going to the stockholders of the Canal Company. The average price paid was $2.20 per acre, and through the auction the company disposed of over 400,000 acres. Since the Canal Company had already sold or traded over 182,000 acres to the Mineral Company and had made other minor sales, its land assets were reduced to less than 150,000 acres. It is probable that Corning converted all his stock into land, since Fairbanks became the new president of the Canal Company after the auction. Woodman agreed to continue serving as land agent for many of the individual owners.[17]

Two months after the Detroit auction, the Boston men formed their own organization, the Michigan Pine Land Association. All the members still held some stock in the Canal Company, although in the articles of association they stated that they had used "a large portion" of this stock to purchase land at the Detroit auction. Each of the twenty-eight members of the association listed the number of Canal Company shares he owned or held in trust for others. Forbes still owned 626 shares outright and held 239 in trust. Thayer held 445 shares, Dennison 300, and Griswold 180. Brooks held 524 shares, an indication that he did not exercise his option to purchase more land. Altogether, the Boston group owned or controlled after the Detroit auction 3,720 shares of the 10,000 shares originally issued. If this constituted a "remaining . . . small amount" of stock after the auction, as the association members said, the canal at Sault Ste. Marie was largely built with Boston capital.[18]

The purpose of the association was quite simple. The members assigned the management and control of all their Michigan pineland to three trustees, Forbes, Brooks, and R. S. Watson. These were empowered to develop the land, build sawmills, sell the land, and even buy more land. The trustees were also given control of all the remaining Canal Company stock held by the members of the association in return for a scrip issue. The trustees thereby gained an important degree of control over the lands still held by the Canal Company; their control increased when, within a few years, Woodman became president of the company, succeeding Fairbanks.[19]

All these transactions meant more work for Woodman. He served as the western land agent for the association, for the Canal Company, and for many of the individual purchasers at Detroit, including Fairbanks. The arrangement must have been complicated for Woodman in an era of slow land sales, but it was very convenient for eastern owners. For example, in 1864 Woodman had the opportunity to dispose of all the pineland holdings along the Pere Marquette River. The Canal Company had sold this land at the auction for over $111,000, with Corning and the Fairbanks brothers each buying about 40 percent and the association buying the rest. By selling the entire tract for $200,000, Woodman made a good profit for the eastern men and a commission for himself. The purchaser of the land was that old friend of the Canal Company, Eber Ward of Detroit. Such windfalls were rare, however. In 1865 Woodman sold only 9,000 acres for the association for $53,772; in the following year he sold 3,000 acres for $26,800. The profits were good, but the process was slow.[20]

Woodman's management problems were considerable, for he represented three classes of absentee owners. Whereas Harvey had once stolen timber from public land with relative impunity, now the problem was reversed. Michigan Canal Superintendent Elisha Calkins reported considerable local hostility as early as 1857, and by the 1860s it was found necessary to keep the pinelands under almost constant supervision to prevent illegal lumbering and theft. Absentee owners were in a vulnerable position. The thieves were more popular than the owners, and Woodman found it difficult to conduct legal prosecutions, since grand juries were reluctant to indict even in the face of conclusive evidence. Woodman also had to worry about vengeful poachers setting forest fires on canal lands in reprisal for lawsuits.[21]

The sale of the pinelands picked up after the Civil War, and in 1874 the Michigan Pine Land Association closed its books. Because the transactions took place over so many years and were so varied in nature, it is impossible to state in full the profits that accrued to the builders of the Sault Canal. Corning still owned western land at the time of his death in 1872, when his fortune was estimated at $8,000,000. The fortunes of Fairbanks and Forbes were involved in too many enterprises to isolate the canal factor of profit, although it is certain that Fairbanks did not suffer through his canal activity. He returned to the governor's chair of Vermont to pledge his fortune to buy uniforms and equipment for the Vermont regiments in the Civil War.[22]

Some of the Mineral Company's ventures were failures, as was the case with the Albany and Boston Mining Company. Other mineral ventures were spectacularly successful. When the Mineral Company traded a mere 480 acres in Houghton County for half the Champion Mining Company stock, the reward in dividends amounted to over 10 times the cost of the canal. It was a reward, however, that went to a new generation and to men who were clever enough to hold on to the Mineral Company stock. It would be a fair, if conservative, estimate to state that the men of Corning's generation probably received $1.50 in return for every $1.00 paid in response to Pruyn's stock calls. As usual, the great fortunes were made by the corporate developers who followed the pioneers, the Calumet and Hecla being the chief example. At least the Canal Company stockholders did not lose their money, although they came dangerously close to it in 1854. In contrast, of the 110 companies organized and mining copper in Michigan before 1925, only 6 paid dividends between 1845 and 1865, these totaling $4,658,000. Almost half this sum was paid by one company, the Pittsburgh and Boston. Fifty-three companies that had launched mining activity before 1865 never paid a single dividend. Finally, of course, the Canal Company added to the value of its own land in the Upper Peninsula through the building of the canal itself.[23]

Epilogue

Erastus Corning and his associates saw their venture at the Sault primarily as a land speculation. When the canal was completed, they had no further interest in it as long as it was not shut down. However, if they believed that the canal itself would bring about an immediate and substantial increase in the value of their land in the Upper Peninsula, they were sorely disappointed. Horace Greeley was correct—more than a canal was needed; but he did not go far enough, and perhaps Corning in the 1850s did not understand the limitations of Greeley's analysis. Indeed, as Greeley wrote, the Upper Peninsula needed not only a canal but human resources and what those resources could provide: capital, labor, roads, docks, harbors. What Greeley failed to understand was that a much-improved technology was required both east and west of the canal before the riches could be grasped.

West of the canal human resources were obviously at work before 1855; and the effort continued unabated after that year, but progress was hampered by poor technology. For example, the "cars" recorded by the canal superintendents as passing westward through the canal destined for the iron fields were little more than large carts to be pulled by mules over one of the crudest rail roads ever constructed. The first steam locomotive did not arrive until 1857, and the need for improved mining technology continued long after that. A decade after the completion of the canal, Alexander Agassiz toiled in the most primitive conditions to bring in the Calumet and Hecla. Since history does not usually record the pathetic failures of small men, there is little knowledge of others who sacrificed as much as Agassiz and lost everything. When Edison and Bell created new markets for copper, modern mining technology finally became available—to the enrichment of the Saint Mary's Canal Mineral Land Company. Corning, however, was dead, and the valuable iron fields had been sold early by the Mineral Company, which had failed to understand that iron ore varies in quality and composition and must therefore be classified. Men in the iron fields in the 1850s who did not grasp this principle or could not apply it risked heavy financial loss.

East of the canal—east to England in fact—the conversion of iron to steel also required a technology not yet developed in 1855. The principle was already understood by a few, including at least one American, William Kelly of Kentucky. Blowing cold air through molten iron to oxidize the unwanted carbon would produce steel. In the early 1850s Kelly tried the process—and produced malleable iron. He could not control the oxidation, and in England Henry Bessemer faced the same problem. Over a decade passed before Americans found the key, some years after Bessemer discovered it.

It was no coincidence that after the advance in steel technology the original canal became obsolete in about a decade. Improved technology both east and west of the canal produced an increasing flow of iron ore, which required larger carriers; these in turn demanded a canal of new proportions. The Army Corps of Engineers took over in 1881 and over the years built four parallel one-lock canals that were much faster and permitted the passage of larger ships. The "Harvey locks" were removed.

Although by World War II the Sault canal system was the most heavily protected installation in the forty-eight states, the canal was an insignificant factor in the Civil War. The war that had begun just six years after the completion of Brooks's work was still a war of men and horses. Again it was the lack of technology rather than iron ore that delayed the exploitation of the mineral wealth of Upper Michigan. When the Union lost the United States armory at Harpers Ferry in 1861, only one government armory remained, in Springfield, Massachusetts. It could turn out only 1,200 rifles per month in the critical manufacturing months of 1861–62. In the same period private concerns in the United States produced fewer than 15,000. The answer was foreign purchase—expensive, often corrupt, but necessary. Meanwhile, changing economic conditions caused a fluctuation in iron ore shipments through the canal (table

2); ore shipments in 1862, the first full year of the Civil War, were less than they had been in 1860.[1]

The economic impact of the canal, though long delayed, was ultimately as significant as its builders could have wished. Its social impact was also significant—and not entirely favorable. Some social loss occurred, and by a stroke of irony the loser was Michigan. In 1862 President Lincoln signed the bill once vetoed by James Buchanan, the Morrill College Land Grant Act. Michigan educators had been among the leaders in demanding the law, which granted large areas of the public domain to support agricultural and mechanical education in each state. According to the census of 1860, Michigan's population entitled the state to six members in the House, and thus it was now entitled to 240,000 acres of land. The land would be used for the benefit of the institution then known as "The Agricultural College of the State of Michigan," now Michigan State University. The problem was that the land must be selected from the public domain in Michigan, where 750,000 acres had already been preempted to build the canal ten years earlier. Lumbering interests had purchased Michigan land in the interim, and the best farmlands in the Lower Peninsula had been sold by the early 1860s. Brooks had once boasted that though the Canal Company could not claim all the excellent timberland available, nothing left over would be better than the company land. His claim was well founded. The Michigan commission under the Morrill Act selected almost all its land in the northern third of the Lower Peninsula, where the Canal Company had already taken 212,000 acres, and the quality of the Morrill land was disappointing. Approximately one-fifth of it was later described as having "no water, no soil, no timber, no grass, no value." Most of the undesirable land was returned to the United States in 1927, but excellent management of the rest of the grant maximized the benefits for Michigan education. Nevertheless, the canal land grant represented a definite social loss.[2]

Overriding the social loss was the major social gain produced by the original canal and its successors, a saving in the cost of steel. Bulk commodities, including iron ore, travel more cheaply by water than by any other means. If, for example, great iron ranges had been found in Nebraska instead of Michigan and Minnesota, American industry would have exploited them just as rapidly; but it would have been more expensive. Cheap, high-quality steel was indispensable to American economic development, and the St. Mary's Falls Canal played a vital role to that end.

Appendix
The Crow of Victory

Utica   June 1. 1855

Hon Erastus Corning

Dear Sir

After bidding you good bye at the Detroit Depot thursday afternoon Governor Fairbanks Attorney General Howard and myself went safely to Lansing arriving there at three o'clock in the morning after a ride over logs that turned our pantaloons into corduroys by the "Stamp Act"

At Lansing we found all the State Officers.— Frost informed us that Mr McKinney was particularly short and crusty— Mr Frost and the State Clerks compared papers in the morning, I joined in this exercise and repeated over "half" "quarter" . . . "North West" and "South East" until my tongue was cut up into quarter sections at all points of the compass.

The governor went to work in his quiet but effective way to adjust the State Scales which at that time acted very much as if they would kick the beam against us. By night the Governor had every State Officer on "Fairbanks Platform" What he said and did I can not tell but I will give you a sample.

After dinner he said to Mr Howard about thus— "Now Sir we have been here all the morning and it is time that we should be informed what to expect from Mr McKinney" Mr Howard replied "I can not control him" to this the Governor answered— "That may be so but the opinion is rife that you can, and the public will hold you responsible"

Remembering our pleasant interview with Mr McKinney on board the Illinois, I kept away from him until I suppose he began to imagine I intended to avoid him. I met him accidentally about 4 o clock in the afternoon and hesitated about shaking hands with him, but he advanced towards me and shook my hand with a decided squeeze, this was such a good symptom that I followed it up by telling him, and Howard, and Jones that we had been unfortunate with Mr McKinney. That while on the boat you thought it best to consult with him as to what might properly be done to expedite our business, and for that purpose I looked him up and found him playing eucre— that I knew it was bad policy to take a man away from a pleasant game to attend to business, but we were obliged to do it.— that the first word he said to you was offensive to you— and that the first word you spoke to him he drew himself up as straight as a friend of mine who some times stood so straight that he fell over backwards—

When I said this he laughed and exclaimed "I won't fall over backwards"

In the midst of this conversation, in came Brooks like a fresh locomotive— the certificates were all on hand. Howard hurried Mr McKinney off to his room, and in half an hour he began to sign and seal the patents.   the mineral first then the pine lands. I drew up a written transfer of the Canal which Mr Howard preferred to the one which he drew. Mr Brooks and I signed and *kept* it until half past seven when Mr McKinney handed me forty patents and then I delivered to him the transfer of the Canal   *the canal was the last thing that was given up—*

Then you never saw happier faces, and you have no idea how friendly all of the State Officers were— they were our warm friends— they had always been.— did not they show us that they would do their duty.—

The next morning they drove to Jackson with us in our wagons— took passes on the railroad from Mr Brooks— and they *fussed* with us in all things, in short, they were the Canal Company and had just got their lands.

Mr McKinney requested me to tell you that you did not understand him on the boat.   that he was not so bad a man after all— in fact he was "all right."—   It is due to Mr Howard to say that from the moment you announced to him— "that it was quite as important for the *State*, that he should go to Lansing as it was for us"— he appeared to act in perfect good faith— indeed I did not present to Mr Howard any paper that he did not agree to without changing a word.—

Mr Brooks made the quickest time to Lansing on record.— When we reached Detroit we found rejoicing and congratulations from all sides except from Sherman, and he swore enough to make every body satisfied that he deserved his defeat—   Saturday night and Sunday I was completely prostrated—   Monday Mr Ledyard gave the 4 governors and us a handsome dinner—   Tuesday Governor Fairbanks Mr Frost and I returned via the Batavia land office—   on Wednesday Governor Fairbanks delivered to Mr Corning 40 patents for 750,000 acres of land and when he did it I thought I could hear some one say — "All right"

Very Truly Yours

John F. Seymour

Notes

For economy of space the following abbreviations have been used in citation:

C. P. — Erastus Corning Papers, Albany Institute of History and Art, Albany, New York

H. P. — Charles Thompson Harvey Papers, J. M. Longyear Research Library, Marquette County Historical Society, Marquette, Michigan

J. P. — James F. Joy Papers, Burton Historical Collection, Detroit Public Library, Detroit, Michigan

L.S.N. & M.J. — *Lake Superior News and Miners' Journal* or *Lake Superior News and Mining Journal*

M.P. & H. — Michigan Pioneer and Historical Collections

S. P. — Horatio Seymour Collection, Collection of Regional History, Cornell University, Ithaca, New York

1. THE YEARS OF FRUSTRATION, 1839–1850.

1. Otto Fowle, *Sault Ste. Marie and Its Great Waterway*, pp. 235, 238; John H. Goff, "History of the Saint Mary's Falls Canal," in *St. Marys Falls Canal Semicentennial, 1905*, ed. Charles Moore, p. 92; Jack L. Hough, *Geology of the Great Lakes*, pp. 3, 5, 35, 45; R. M. Lane, J. E. Johnston, and L. Sitgreaves, "Survey of Fort Brady," *Field Book*, Office, Chief of Engineers, Record Group 77, The National Archives, Washington, D.C.; Charles R. Van Hise, *The Conservation of Natural Resources in the United States*, p. 33; Alvah Bradish, *Memoir of Douglass Houghton*, p. 277.

2. Hough, *Geology of the Great Lakes*, pp. 267–68.

3. Ibid., pp. 14, 81; Charles R. Van Hise and Charles Kenneth Leith, *The Geology of the Lake Superior Region*, Plate I; Leland Horberg and Richard C. Anderson, "Bedrock Topography and Pleistocene Glacial Lobes in Central United States," pp. 104, 110; Bradish, *Memoir of Houghton*, p. 170; State of Michigan, *Michigan Joint Documents, 1841* (Detroit, 1841), pp. 483–84.

4. Elizabeth F. Ellet, *Summer Rambles in the West*, p. 239; State of Michigan, *Documents to Accompany the Journal of the House of Representatives of Michigan, 1838* (Detroit, 1838), p. 570; *Michigan State Documents, 1838* (Detroit, 1838), No. 32.

5. For the complete story of this fiasco, see Clark F. Norton, "Early Movement for St. Mary's Falls Ship Canal," pp. 257–80.

6. United States, *Biographical Directory of the American Congress, 1774–1961*, p. 1395.

7. *Congressional Globe*, 25th Cong., 3d sess., 7 January 1839, p. 103, 16 January 1839, p. 127; ibid., 26th Cong., 1st sess., 4 December 1839, p. 12, 16 December 1839, p. 54, 31 December 1839, p. 92, 3 January 1840, p. 99.

8. Ibid., 26th Cong., 1st sess., 6 April 1840, pp. 306–7; Michigan Pioneer and Historical Society, comp., *Michigan Pioneer and Historical Collections*, 2:360 (hereafter cited as M.P. & H.); J. Almy, "Survey for a Ship Canal Around the Falls of St. Mary," Canals 295-1, Record Group No. 77, Cartographic Section, Archives.

9. *Congressional Globe*, 26th Cong., 1st sess., 9 April 1840, p. 310.

10. Ibid., 14 April 1840, p. 325, 21 April 1840, Appendix, pp. 828–29.

11. Ibid., 21 April 1840, pp. 349–51, 828–29.

12. Ibid., 21 April 1840, pp. 349–51.

13. Ibid., 21 April 1840, p. 342, 30 April 1840, p. 368. Unfortunately no formal roll call was recorded.

14. Ibid., 30 December 1839, p. 88, 10 February 1840, p. 180, 14 February 1840, p. 200; ibid., 2d sess., 9 December 1840, p. 184; *Cong. Biog. Dir.*, p. 750.

15. State of Michigan, *Documents Accompanying the Journal of the House of Michigan, 1840*, 2 vols. (Detroit, 1840), II, pp. 176–77, 462–66.

16. State of New York, *Documents of the Assembly of the State of New York, 1843*, 4 vols. (Albany, 1843), IV, No. 103; State of Ohio, *Documents, Messages and Other Communications Made to the Forty First General Assembly of the State of Ohio*, 7 vols. (Columbus, 1843), VII, No. 56; State of Michigan, *Joint Documents of the Legislature of the State of Michigan, 1877*, 5 vols. (Lansing, 1878), III, p. 5.

17. United States, Department of the Interior, B. S. Butler and W. S. Burbank, *The Copper Deposits of Michigan*, Professional Paper No. 144 (Washington, 1929); Roy M. Robbins, *Our Landed Heritage*, p. 142; Robert James Hybels, "The Lake Superior Copper Fever, 1841–1847," p. 231; Francis Paul Prucha, *A Guide to the Military Posts of the United States*, p. 116.

18. Hybels, "Copper Fever," p. 231; Ralph D. Williams, *The Honorable Peter White: A Biographical Sketch of the Lake Superior Iron Country*, pp. 114–15, 117; M. P. & H., 21:357; United States, *Senate Executive Documents*, 29th Cong., 1st sess., IV, No. 160.

19. F. A. Barnard, comp., *American Biographical History of Eminent and Self-Made Men*, pp. 6, 93–94; S. D. Bingham, comp., *Early History of Michigan with Biographies*, p. 372; M. P. & H., 17:179, 4:389–91.

20. *Lake Superior News and Miners' Journal* (Copper Harbor, Michigan), July 11, 1846 (hereafter cited as *L. S. N. & M. J.*).

21. *New York Daily Tribune*, 22 June 1847; Prucha, *Guide to Military Posts*, p. 116.

22. Prucha, *Guide to Military Posts*, pp. 61–62; John R. St. John, *A True Description of the Lake Superior Country*, pp. 18–19; Charles Lanman, *A Summer in the Wilderness; Embracing a Canoe Voyage up the Mississippi and Around Lake Superior*, pp. 157, 161; Benjamin H. Hibbard, *A History of the Public Land Policies*, p. 23; "Map of Part of Township 47N, Ranges 1E, and 1W, Michigan Meridian," Canals 137-18, Record Group 77, Cartographic Section, Archives.

23. *New York Daily Tribune*, 24 June July 2, 1847; *L. S. N. & M. J.*, 3, 10 July 1847. The Weed editorial was cited by Ingersoll on 21 August 1847, and by Greeley on 23 July 1847. Paul M. Angle, ed., "The Western Trip of Philip Hone," pp. 292–94; Lanman, *Summer in Wilderness*, p. 157.

24. *New York Daily Tribune*, 10, 12, 13 July 1847.

25. *L. S. N. & M. J.*, 30 June, 10, 26 August, 13 October 1848; Louis Agassiz, *Lake Superior: Its Physical Character, Vegetation, and Animals* . . . *with a Narrative of the Tour by J. Elliot Cabot*, pp. v, 33–34, 30–32; Edward Lurie, *Louis Agassiz; A Life in Science*, pp. 148–49.

26. *L. S. N. & M. J.*, 10 July 1847; *Lake Superior Journal* (Sault Ste. Marie, Michigan), 23, 30 July 1851; Charles E. Rosenberg, *The Cholera Years*, p. 40; M. P. & H., 9:109.

27. James D. Richardson, comp., *A Compilation of the Messages and Papers of the Presidents of the United States, 1789–1897*, 4:460.

28. Ibid., pp. 462, 464, 465.

29. Bayard Tuckerman, ed., *The Diary of Philip Hone*, 2:309; *L. S. N. & M. J.*, 3 July 1847.

30. Mentor L. Williams, "The Background of the Chicago River and Harbor Convention, 1847," pp. 219–20, 228; *New York Weekly Tribune*, 19 June 1847; United States, *House Executive Documents*, 29th Cong., 1st sess., No. 2, p. 222; Larry Gara, *Westernized Yankee: The Story of Cyrus Woodman*, pp. 71–72.

31. Robert Fergus, Comp., "Chicago River and Harbor Convention," p. 14; *L. S. N. & M. J.*, 3 July 1847.

32. Ronald E. Shaw, *Erie Water West: A History of the Erie Canal, 1792–1854*, pp. 349–51, 307; *New York Daily Tribune*, 13, 15 July 1847; Fergus, "River and Harbor Convention," pp. 69–78.

33. *L. S. N. & M. J.*, 10 July 1847; *Daily Albany Argus* (Albany, New York), 13 July 1847; Fergus, "River and Harbor Convention," pp. 81–84.

34. United States, *Senate Miscellaneous Documents*, 30th Cong., 1st sess., No. 146.

35. Richardson, *Messages and Papers*, 4:610–26.

36. Robbins, *Landed Heritage*, p. 160; Williams R. D., "River and Harbor Convention," p. 622; Freeman Hunt, ed., *The Merchants' Magazine and Commercial Review* (New York), 17 (August 1847): 217–18; *New York Daily Tribune*, 23 July 1847; *Albany Evening Journal*, 14 July 1847; *L. S. N. & M. J.*, 21 August 1847, 28 October 1848; *Daily Herald* (Cleveland, Ohio), 17 July 1852.

2.   FAILURE OF STATE FINANCING AND AN ACT OF CONGRESS

1. Harry N. Scheiber, *Ohio Canal Era: A Cast Study of Government and the Economy, 1820–1861*, pp. 111–12, 135.

2. Willis Frederick Dunbar, *Michigan Through the Centuries*, 1:200–211; Frederick Clever Bald, *Michigan in Four Centuries*, pp. 212–26; Shaw, *Erie Water West*, p. 262; Robert J. Parks, *Democracy's Railroads: Public Enterprise in Jacksonian Michigan*, p. 31.

3. Parks, *Democracy's Railroads*, pp. 10–11, 68.

4. Ibid., p. 85.

5. Ibid., pp. 106, 181; Carter Goodrich, "The Revulsion against Internal Improvements," pp. 147, 152, 161.

6. Ben Perley Poore, comp., *The Federal and State Constitutions, Colonial Charters, and Other Organic Laws of the United States*, 1:1008.

7. Parks, *Democracy's Railroads*, pp. 105, 130.

8. United States, *Census of 1850* (Washington, 1853); State of Michigan, *Joint Documents of the Legislature of the State of Michigan, 1850* (Detroit, 1850), pp. 50–59. United States, House Executive Documents, 31st Cong., 1st sess., IX, No. 69, pp. 146–51; United States, *Senate Executive Documents*, 31st cong., 1st sess., III, No. 1, pp. 387, 612–15, 760–65.

9. *L. S. N. & M. J.*, 8 September, 10, 28 October 1848.

10. State of Michigan, *Journal of the Senate of Michigan, 1849* (Detroit, 1849), pp. 433, 476, 603, 648; *L. S. N. & M. J.*, 8 June, 29 September 1849; State of Michigan, *Joint Documents, 1850*, p. 59; United States, *Senate Executive Documents*, 31st Cong., 1st sess., III, p. 611.

11. *L. S. N. & M. J.*, 14 July, 10 October, 11 November 1848, 8 November 1849; Bingham, *History of Michigan*, p. 372; M. P. & H., 28:426.

12. *Lake Superior Journal* (Sault Ste. Marie and Detroit, Michigan), 1 May, 19 June 1850.

13. *Lake Superior Journal*, 1 December 1851; Brown published in Detroit in the winter of 1851–52. Israel D. Andrews, in his "Report on the Trade and Commerce of the British North American Colonies and upon the Trade of the Great Lakes and Rivers," United States, *Senate Documents*, 32d Cong., 1st sess., No. 112, p. 51, must have assumed that the rapids constituted a complete block; he reported no steamships on Lake Superior. James L. Barton, in *Lake Commerce, Letter to the Hon. Robert McClelland*, pp. 19, 30, reported one large propeller on Lake Superior out of the sixty steamships on the Great Lakes above Niagara Falls in 1846.

14. *Lake Superior Journal*, 1 August, 8, 24 October 1851.

15. Ibid., 5 November, 1 December 1851.

16. Holman Hamilton, *Zachary Taylor*, 2:158, 300, 327, 364.

17. Ibid., p. 403.

18. *Detroit Free Press*, 6, 9, 12 January 1852; *Lake Superior Journal*, 2 February 1852.

19. *The Daily Plain Dealer* (Cleveland, Ohio), 15 January, 6 February 1852; State of Indiana, *Journal of the Indiana State Senate: 36 sess., 1851–1852* (Indianapolis, 1852), p. 562; State of New York, *Journal of the Senate of the State of New York, 75 sess., 1852* (Albany, 1852), pp. 213, 487; *Detroit Free Press*, 6 March 1852; M. P. & H., 21:360; Williams, R. D., *White*, p. 121

20. Hamilton, *Taylor*, 2:277; Walter W. Stevens, "Lewis Cass and the Presidency," pp. 133–34; Frank B. Woodford, *Lewis Cass*, p. 267; *New York Daily Tribune*, 10 June 1852; *Detroit Daily Advertiser*, 19 August 1852.

21. *Congressional Globe*, 32d Cong., 1st sess., 11 August 1852, p. 2185, 13 August 1852, p. 2201, 16 August 1852, p. 2227, Appendix, p. 944.

22. Ibid., 16 August 1852, p. 2232.

23. Ibid.

24. Ibid., 25 August 1852, pp. 2348–49.

25. Ibid.

26. For the case against oversimplification, see Joel H. Silbey, "The Civil War Synthesis in American Political History," pp. 130–40.

27. United States, *Statutes at Large and Treaties of the United States of America from December 1, 1851 to March 3, 1855*, 10 vols. (Boston, 1855), 5: 35–36; William T. Young, *The Life of Lewis Cass*, p. 84; "Map of Part of Townships 47N, Ranges 1E, and 1W, Michigan Meridian," Archives.

28. United States, *Statutes at Large*, 5: 35–36. For a general summary of federal grants for

canal construction, see John Bell Rae, "Federal Land Grants in Aid of Canals," pp. 167–77.

3. RUSHED PLANS AND HURRIED ESTIMATES

1. Cleveland *Daily Herald*, 17, 18, 21, 27 August 1852; *Detroit Daily Advertiser*, 20 August 1852; *Lake Superior Journal*, 25 August, 8 September 1852.

2. *Lake Superior Journal*, 15 September 1852.

3. Ibid.; "Life History of Charles Thompson Harvey," unsigned but probably written by Sarah Van Eps Harvey (hereafter cited as H. P.). This account can be trusted for Harvey's age and little more.

4. Hiram Carleton, comp., *Genealogical and Family History of the State of Vermont*, pp. 109–18. Hereafter all references to Fairbanks will omit the given name unless the reference is to Thaddeus or Joseph.

5. Fairbanks to Corning, 31 May, 28 July, 12 August, 25 December 1852, Erastus Corning Papers, Albany Institute of History and Art, Albany, New York (hereafter cited as C. P.).

6. Irene D. Neu, *Erastus Corning: Merchant and Financier*, pp. 18, 42, 89, 101, 115, 129; H. M. Walker to Watts Sherman, 17 May 1852; David Wagner to Corning, 12 August 1852; S. B. Jewett to Corning, 23 June 1852; William McAlpine to Corning, 12 August 1852; G. C. Davidson to Corning, 20 July 1852, all in C. P.

7. Fairbanks to Corning, 16 November 1852, C. P.

8. Ibid.; Harvey to Fairbanks, 31 August 1851, H. P.

9. Harvey to Brown, 17 October 1852, Plaintiff Exhibit No. 3, *St. Mary's Falls Ship Canal Company* v. *Joseph V. Brown*, Wayne County Circuit Court, Chancery No. 608, Old County Building, Detroit, Michigan (hereafter cited as *Canal Co.* v *Brown*).

10. State of New York, *Supplement to the Annual Report of the State Engineer and Surveyor of the State of New York*, 2 vols. (Albany, New York, 1906), 2:1143. Shaw, *Erie Water West*, p. 362.

11. Nichols to E. & T. Fairbanks Co., 9 December 1852, Horatio Seymour Collection, Collection of Regional History, Cornell University, Ithaca, New York (hereafter cited as S. P.); Harvey to Brown, 13 January 1853, Plaintiff Exhibit No. 1, *Canal Co.* v *Brown*.

12. Carter Goodrich, "American Development Policy: The Case of Internal Improvements," 1:354.

13. This general engineering comparison used Canfield's study, which was the one most recently available to the Sault canal builders before the beginning of their work; Augustus Canfield to Robert McClelland (no day or month), 1852, Topographical Bureau, Record Group No. 77, Archives. For the engineering data on the Erie Canal, I am indebted to Shaw, *Erie Water West*, pp. 87, 126–30, 134–35, and to many conversations with Professor Shaw.

14. Canfield estimated that the cost of the Sault construction would be $557,739.10 in Canfield to McClelland, 1852, Archives; Shaw, *Erie Water West*, p. 192.

15. For the story of this canal, see Paul Fatout, "Canal Agitation at Ohio Falls," pp. 279–309; and Paul B. Trescott, "The Louisville and Portland Canal Company, 1825–1874," pp. 686–708.

16. Neu, *Corning*, p. 181; Shaw, *Erie Water West*, pp. 381, 379, 86.

17. Thomas C. Cochran, *Railroad Leaders, 1845–1890*, pp. 37–38, 91.

18. *Lake Superior Journal*, 6 October 1852.

19. *Louisville Courier* (Louisville, Kentucky), 28 July 1853.

20. George W. Cullum, comp., *Biographical Register of the Officers and Graduates of the*

United States Military Academy, 1:283; Canfield and Burt, "Map of the Canal at Saut Ste. Marie, 1853," Canals 88, Record Group No. 77, Cartographic Sections, Archives; Woodford, *Cass*, p. 296. Upon his return to Detroit from the Sault, Canfield found it necessary to explain to his superior officer why he had left his post without permission. This he did in Canfield to Abert, 13 October 1852, Topographic Bureau, Record Group No. 77, M-506, Archives. In this letter Canfield also described McClelland's dilemma when he could not get help from the secretary of war.

21. This and the technical information that follows can be found in map, Canfield to Abert, 13 October 1852, and in Canfield to McClelland (no day or month), 1852, "Description of canal and estimate of cost," 19 pages, both in Archives.

22. The reader can well be amused at Canfield's practice of admitting to guesswork on several important items and then carrying out his estimate to the last dime; Canfield to Abert, December 9, 2, 1852, Archives; Daniel H. Calhoun, *American Civil Engineers*, pp. 68, 164.

23. *Washtenaw Whig* (Ann Arbor, Michigan), 9 January 1853.

4.   LEGISLATION AND A CONTRACT

1. Woodford, *Cass*, p. 294; Henry Greenleafe Pearson, *An American Railroad Builder, John Murray Forbes*, p. 53; *Detroit Daily Advertiser*, 29 September, 27 October 1852.

2. Alfred D. Chandler, Jr., *Henry Varnum Poor: Business Editor, Analyst, and Reformer*, p. 150.

3. Neu, *Corning*, p. 73; Cochran, *Railroad Leaders*, p. 165.

4. Joy to Corning, 21 December 1852, C. P.; Corning to Brooks and Joy, 15 December 1852, James Frederick Joy Papers, Burton Historical Collection, Detroit Public Library, Detroit, Michigan (hereafter cited as J. P.).

5. M. P. & H., 22:301, 303–4, 21:257–58; Pearson, *Forbes*, p. 47; Sarah Forbes Hughes, ed., *Letters and Recollections of John Murray Forbes*, 2:212; Cochran, *Railroad Leaders*, p. 38.

6. Williams, *White*, p. 122; *Lake Superior Journal*, 6 October 1852; Harlan Hatcher, *A Century of Iron and Men*, pp. 21–24; Canfield to McClelland, "Description of Canal"; M. P. & H., 18:342.

7. John Burt to William Austin Burt, 3 January 1853, Burt Papers, J. M. Longyear Research Library. Unfortunately John Burt did not name those attending the meeting, but it is reasonable to assume that Joy was at least represented since he knew so much about it.

8. Harvey to Corning, 6 January 1853, C. P. Harvey was never backward when it came to claiming credit. However, the canal bill resembled closely the description that Harvey had given to Brown the previous fall, so Harvey probably had drafted the bill. E. Peck to Joy, 29 January 1853; Joy to Porter, 8, 13, 14 January 1853, both in J. P.

9. Harvey to Corning, 6, 19 January 1853, C. P.

10. Harvey to Corning, 19 January 1853, C. P.; *Detroit Daily Advertiser*, 20 January 1853.

11. Ward to William Burt, 13 January 1853, as cited in Williams, *White*, pp. 123–24; *Lake Superior Journal*, 13 October 1852; *Washtenaw Whig*, 9, 23 February 1853; Bruce Catton, *Michigan: A Bicentenial History*, pp. 120–21.

12. State of Michigan, *Acts of the Legislature of the State of Michigan Passed at the Regular Session of 1853* (Lansing, 1853), No. 38, pp. 48–51.

13. Ibid., No. 61, pp. 86–87.

14. Neu, *Corning*, pp. 83–85, 164; Corning to Joy, 23 August 1852, J. P.; Brooks to Corning, 6, 23 February 1853, C. P.

15. Harvey to Corning, 26 February 1853, C. P.

16. Brooks to Corning, 19 March 1853, C. P.; Harvey to Joy, 21 February 1853, J. P.

17. Joy to Corning, 24 March 1853, C. P.; Telegram, Harvey to Joy, 26 March 1853; Bronson to Joy, 30 March 1853; Brooks to Joy, 30 March 1853, all in J. P.

18. *Detroit Free Press*, 3 April 1853; Canfield to Abert, 4 April 1853, Archives; "August Belmont," *Dictionary of American Biography*; *National Cyclopedia of American Biography*, 13:446–47; M. P. & H., 4:475.

19. Brooks to Corning, 5 April 1853, C. P.; Peter Beckman, "James F. Joy and the Western Railroads," chaps. 4, 16. Beckman cited Bronson to Joy, 12 April 1853, and Joy to Bronson, 16 April 1853, Bronson Papers (Martin Collection, New York Public Library); *New York Daily Tribune*, 16 April 1853; Bronson to Corning, 13 April 1853, C. P.

20. Brown to Harvey, 28 February 1853, Plaintiff Exhibit "C"; undated, unsigned letter in Brown's handwriting headed "Read and Burn," Plaintiff Exhibit "E"; Certificate signed by Parsons, 5 April 1853, Plaintiff Exhibit "B," all in *Canal Co. v. Brown*.

21. Harvey to Brown, 13 January 1853, Plaintiff Exhibit No. 1; Harvey to Brown, 10 April 1853, Plaintiff Exhibit No. 2; Deposition of Plaintiff and Response of Defendant, all in *Canal Co. v. Brown*.

22. Brown to Harvey, 12 April 1853, Plaintiff Exhibit "D"; Response of Defendant, both in *Canal Co. v. Brown*; Harvey to Corning, 6 April 1853, C. P.

23. Roy F. Nichols, *Franklin Pierce*, pp. 206, 214, 218. A large number of job applications preserved in the Corning Papers came at this time.

24. Weed's editorial for the canal was mentioned in the *L. S. N. & M. J.*, 21 August 1847, and was reprinted in full in the *New York Daily Tribune*, 23 July 1847; Glyndon G. Van Deusen, *Thurlow Weed: Wizard of the Lobby*, p. 85; *Congressional Globe*, 32d Cong., 1st sess., 16 August 1852, p. 2232; Neu, *Corning*, p. 164; Harvey to Joy, 16 April 1853, J. P.

25. Hereafter cited as the Canal Company.

26. State of New York, *New York Laws, 1853*, ch. 180, pp. 316–20.

27. Joy to Porter, 28 April 1853; Telegrams, Joy to Harvey and Joy to Porter, 29 April 1853, all in J. P.

28. Telegram, Joy to Corning, 14 May 1853, C. P.; Joy to Porter, 16 May 1853; Brooks to Joy, 20 May 1853, both in J. P.; *Detroit Free Press*, 16 May 1853.

29. Joy to Corning, 21 January 1851, C. P.; Frank Walker Stevens, *The Beginnings of the New York Central Railroad*, pp. 326, 373, 382; Neu, *Corning*, pp. 163–64.

30. "Notice to Stockholders," 30 April 1853; Brooks to Corning, 28 April 1853; Fairbanks to Corning, 9 May 1853; O. S. M. Ballon to Corning, 2 May 1853, all in C. P. Brooks to Joy, 28 April 1853; Pruyn to Joy, 30 April 1853, both in J. P.

31. Forbes to Corning, 22 March 1853; Telegram, Forbes to Corning, 13 May 1853; Brooks to Corning, 23 August 1854, all in C. P.; Pruyn to Joy, 23 June 1853, J. P.; Cochran, *Railraod Leaders*, p. 104; Chandler, *Poor*, p. 101; Certificate of Pruyn, 6 March 1856, Plaintiff Exhibit "F," *Canal Co. v. Brown*.

32. Williams, *White*, p. 130; Neu, *Corning*, p. 164; Telegram, Harvey to Joy, 17 May 1853; Harvey to Joy and Porter, 21 May 1853, both in J. P.; Forbes to Corning, 17 May 1853; Telegram, Seymour to Corning, 23 May 1853, both in C. P.

33. Neu, *Corning*, pp. 3–4, 16–18, 35; Corning to Brooks, 12 January 1847, and Brooks to Forbes, 10 September 1847, as cited in Cochran, *Railroad Leaders*, pp. 303, 82.

34. Contract between the State of Michigan and Fairbanks, Forbes, Corning, Belmont, Dwight, et al., "Sureties," Archives, Historical Commission, State of Michigan, Lansing, Michigan.

5. COMPLACENCY, 1853

1. Canfield to Abert, 1 July 1853, Archives; *Lake Superior Journal*, 11 June 1853; State of Michigan, *Documents Accompanying the Journal of the Senate of the State of Michigan, 1849* (Detroit, 1859), pp. 17–18. Chapel to Joy and Porter, 4 June 1852, J. P.; Michigan State Historical Commission, comp., *Michigan Biographies*, 1:382; Waterman, Watkins & Co., comp., *History of Cass County, Michigan* (Chicago, 1882), p. 279. Glenn's rank was either of the state militia or honorary. He was not a United States officer.

2. United States, *Senate Documents*, 33d Cong., 1st sess., 1853, III, No. 1, p. 17; Canfield acknowledged receipt of the order and restated it in Canfield to Abert, 4 April 1853, Archives; Brooks to Corning, 10 March 1853, C. P.; Brooks to Joy, 23 April 1853, J. P. I have not been able to determine when, if ever, Canfield revealed his orders to Harvey and Nichols.

3. *Lake Superior Journal*, 11, 18 June 1853.

4. Neu, *Corning*, p. 168; G. C. Davidson to Corning, 3 June 1852, C. P.; Cochran, *Railroad Leaders*, pp. 25, 116.

5. "Bookkeeper's Report," L. T. Merrill to Fairbanks, 24 March 1855, H. P.; Harvey to Joy, 22 September, 23 August 1853, J. P.

6. Brooks to Corning, 1 August 1853, C. P.; *Lake Superior Journal*, 3 September, 2 July 1853.

7. Brooks to Joy, 5 November 1853, 17 July 1854, J. P.; Robbins, *Landed Heritage*, pp. 125, 127. The nearest that any Canal Company officer came to describing the laborers as immigrants was in a letter, Brooks to Seymour, 30 September 1854, S. P., to be quoted in proper context. Men like Brooks had not the slightest interest in the background of the workers. They were hired to do a job and discarded when it was over. Nevertheless it is reasonable to assume that immigrant labor contributed to the building of the canal.

8. *Lake Superior Journal*, 15 August 1853; Harvey to President and Directors, 6 August 1853, J. P.; Shaw, *Erie Water West*, p. 91; *The Evening News* (Sault Ste. Marie, Michigan), 2 August 1905: Brooks to Fairbanks, 22 August 1854, H. P.; Corning to Charles Moran, 12 November 1857, as cited in Cochran, *Railroad Leaders*, p. 304; *Daily Plain Dealer*, 4 May 1854; Frost to Whitwood, 8 October 1853, J. P.

9. Fairbanks to Corning, 23 May 1853; Pruyn to Corning, 6 June 1853, both in C. P.; A/C, Harvey with Canal Company, 1 August 1853, J. P.

10. Nichols to President and Directors, 6 August 1853; Harvey to President and Directors, 6 August 1853, both in J. P.; Harvey to Seymour, 6 August 1853, S. P. It was obvious from his letters that Harvey was most pleased with the way in which he handled the strike.

11. Harvey to Seymour, 6 August 1853, S. P.; Harvey to President and Directors, 6 August 1853, J. P.; Brooks to Corning, 1 August 1853, C. P.

12. Harvey to Seymour, 6 August 1853, S. P.; Harvey to President and Directors, 6 August 1853, J. P.

13. Brown to Harvey, 12 April 1853, Plaintiff Exhibit "B," *Canal Co.* v. *Brown*; E. Tavirrent to Corning, 16 June 1853, C. P.; "Harvey Claims," 21 June 1853, Records of the General Office, Selection and Adjustment Lists, 1850–1921, Division F, Record Group 49, Archives; Harvey to Joy, 28 July 1853, J. P.; *Daily Evening Star* (Washington, D.C.), 5, 7, 25 October, 14 November 1853; Nichols, *Pierce*, p. 253.

14. *Lake Superior Journal*, 13 August 1853.

15. Canfield to Abert, 4 August, 30 September, 2 October 1853, Archives; Harvey to Joy, 23 August, 22 September 1853, J. P.

16. United States, *Army Meteorological Register, 1843–1854* (Washington, 1855), Reports from Fort Brady, pp. 454 *et seq.*; *Lake Superior Journal*, 2, 16 July 1854.

17. Nichols to President and Directors, 15 September 1853, J. P.

18. Harvey to Joy, 22 September 1853, J. P.

19. Canfield to Abert, 30 September 1853, Archives; *Lake Superior Journal*, 29 November 1853.

20. Harvey to Corning, 5 November 1853, C. P.; Deposition of Harvey, 19 May 1856, *Canal Co. v. Brown*. Harvey claimed full authority over all phases of the project at all times in this deposition, and he continued to do so for the rest of his life; others eventually came to believe him. See East Tablet of the fiftieth Centennial Monument, Sault Ste. Marie, Michigan; Goff, "History of Canal," p. ix; or Bald, *Michigan*, pp. 244–45. Credit for the discovery of Harvey's exaggerations of his authority goes to Ernest H. Rankin, "Canalside Superintendent," pp. 103–14.

21. Harvey to Fairbanks, 12 January 1854, H. P.

22. Pruyn to Directors, 23 November 1853; Read to Corning, 4 November 1853; Brooks to Corning, 4 November 1853, all in C. P.; Brooks to Clark, 10 December 1853; Brooks to Fairbanks, 4 January 1854; Clark to Brooks, 15 December 1853, all in H. P. New York, *Report of State Engineer*, I, p. 192, II, p. 1144.

23. My italics. *Lake Superior Journal*, 2 January 1854; Harvey to Whitwood, 5 January 1854, J. P.; Harvey to Fairbanks, 12 January 1854, H. P.; *Daily Plain Dealer*, 10 May 1854.

24. *Daily Plain Dealer*, 10 May 1854; Harvey to Fairbanks, 12 January 1854, H. P.; State of Michigan, "Report of the Auditor General," *Joint Documents of the State of Michigan, 1853* (Detroit, 1853), p. 8.

6. COURTING DISASTER, 1854

1. *Lake Superior Journal*, 2 January 1854; Harvey to Joy, 1 January 1854, J. P.; Canfield to Abert, 10 March 1854, Archives. As was his practice, Canfield reviewed the entire sequence of events in his report to Abert to explain to him why he had not obeyed orders immediately.

2. Canfield to Abert, 10 March 1854, Archives.

3. United States, *Acts Passed in the First Session of the Eighteenth Congress of the United States* (Washington, 1824), ch. 46, p. 35; United States, *Senate Executive Documents, 1853*, 33d Cong., 1st sess., III, p. 17, II, p. 27; Nichols, *Pierce*, pp. 295–96; Forest G. Hill, *Roads, Rails, & Waterways: The Army Engineer and Early Transportation*, pp. 46–49.

4. Canfield to Abert, 10 March 1854, Archives; Chandler, *Poor*, p. 76; Nichols, *Pierce*, p. 214; Brooks to Fairbanks, 24 March 1854, H. P. I have not been able to determine if the Thayer brothers held any stock in the Canal Company at this time, but it is quite possible that they did. It was significant that Brooks, in Detroit, should be the one to tell Fairbanks what went on behind the doors of the White House. The assumption is that John Thayer or Forbes told him.

5. Canfield to Abert, 10 March 1854, Archives.

6. *Detroit Free Press*, 18, 19 April 1854.

7. Brooks to Corning, 20, 21 January, 10 April, 27 May 1854, C. P.; New York, *Report of State Engineer*, II, p. 1160; *Lake Superior Journal*, 17 May 1854.

8. Harvey to Joy, 12 January 1854, J. P.; Harvey to Corning, 22 March 1854; Fairbanks to Corning, 22 March 1854, both in C. P.; Brooks to Fairbanks, 20 April, 1 May 1854, H. P.

9. Brooks to Corning, 27 January 1854, C. P.; Joy to Forbes, 6 February 1854, J. P.; Brooks to Fairbanks, 24 March 1854, H. P.

10. *Daily Plain Dealer*, 25 March 1854; United States, *Army Meteorological Register*, pp. 454 *et seq.*; Harvey to Fairbanks, 4 April 1854, H. P.; Harvey to Seymour, 15 April 1854, S. P.

11. Fairbanks to Corning, 12 April 1854; Brooks to Corning, 25 April 1854, both in C. P.

12. Nichols to Directors, 15 April 1854, S. P.

13. Brooks to Fairbanks, 20 April 1854, H. P.

14. A/C, Seymour with Canal Company, June 1854, to February 1856, S. P.; Fairbanks to Corning, 7 June 1854, C. P.; Harvey to Fairbanks, 1 July 1854, H. P.; *Detroit Free Press*, 15 June 1854; *Lake Superior Journal*, 24 May 1854; United States, Bureau of Land Management, "Falls of the St. Mary's River, 1852," Record Group 49, Archives.

15. M. P. & H., 22:301; Cochran, *Railroad Leaders*, p. 37.

16. Harvey to Seymour, 15 April 1854, S. P.; Fairbanks to Corning, 7 June 1854, C. P.

17. Telegrams, Brooks to Corning, 10 May 1854, and Davidson to Corning, 11 May 1854; Brooks to Corning, 10 May 1854, all in C. P.; Neu, *Corning*, p. 70; Telegram, Brooks to Joy, 15 May 1854, J. P.

18. *Lake Superior Journal*, 10 June 1854; United States, Department of Engineering, "Detailed Drawings of St. Mary's Falls Canal and Locks, Michigan" (Washington, 1882–84); Brooks to Joy, 15 May 1854, J. P.

19. Nichols, "Estimate of Work Done and to be Done," 6 June 1854, S. P.; Fairbanks to Corning, 7 June 1854, C. P.

20. Fairbanks to Corning, 7 June 1854, C. P.

21. *Daily Plain Dealer*, 30 June 1854; Harvey to Fairbanks, 1 July 1854; Brooks to Fairbanks, 21 July 1854, both in H. P.; *Lake Superior Journal*, 8 July 1854.

22. Brooks to Joy, 15 July 1854, J. P.

23. Cochran, *Railroad Leaders*, pp. 110–11; Brooks to Joy, 17 July 1854, J. P.; Brooks to Fairbanks, 22 July 1854, H. P.

24. A/C, Seymour with Canal Company; Agreement between John Seymour and John Richardson, 2 August 1854, S. P.; Brooks to Corning, 3 August 1854, C. P.

25. Rosenberg, *The Cholera Years*, pp. 56, 120.

26. Fairbanks to Corning, 7 June 1854, C. P.; Porter to Joy, 10 June 1854, J. P.; *Detroit Free Press*, 15 June 1854; *Daily Plain Dealer*, 30 June 1854; *Lake Superior Journal*, 8, 29 July 1854.

27. *Lake Superior Journal*, 5 July, 2, 9, September, 14 October 1854.

28. Brooks to Joy, 23 August 1854, J. P.; *Lake Superior Journal*, 12, 26 August 1854; Williams, *White*, pp. 86, 132–33; Cochran, *Railroad Leaders*, p. 38; unsigned letter to stockholders, 13 October 1854, S. P.; United States, Office of the Adjutant General, Post Returns, Record Group 94, Archives; United States, *Army Meteorological Register*, pp. 454 *et seq.*

29. A/C, D. B. Waterman, Jr., with Canal Company; Martin White to Seymour, 22 December 1854, both in S. P.

30. Brooks to Seymour, 30 September 1854; Whitwood to Seymour, 28 September 1854, both in S. P.

31. Pearson, *Forbes*, p. 99; Cochran, *Railroad Leaders*, pp. 37–38; Brooks to Joy, 23 August 1854, J. P.; *Daily Plain Dealer*, 22 July 1854.

32. Brooks to Fairbanks, 22 July 1854, H. P.; *Lake Superior Journal*, 5 August 1854.

33. *Lake Superior Journal*, 8 July 1854; *Detroit Free Press*, 9 July 1854.

34. Whitwood to Seymour, 28 September 1854, S. P.

35. *Lake Superior Journal*, 14 October 1854; unsigned letter to stockholders, 13 October 1854, S. P.

36. Harvey to Fairbanks, 28 October 1854, H. P.; *Lake Superior Journal*, 9 September 1854.

37. *Lake Superior Journal*, 4 November 1854; Brooks to Corning, 4 November 1854, C. P.; Brooks to Joy, 9 November 1854, J. P.

38. Brooks to Corning, 4, 9 November 1854; Fairbanks to Corning, 20, 27 November 1854, both in C. P.; Brooks to Joy, 26 October, 9 November 1854; Harvey to Joy, 30 October 1854, both in J. P.; *Lake Superior Journal*, 4 November 1854; *Daily Plain Dealer*, 29 November 1854; United States, *Army Meteorological Register*, pp. 454 *et seq.*

39. Utley and Cutcheon, *Michigan*, III, p. 359; M. P. & H., 17:253–54; "Horatio Seymour," *Dictionary of American Biography*, 9:6–9.

40. Brooks to Joy, 17 May 1854, J. P.; Seymour to Corning, 20, 22 November 1854, C. P.; *Daily Plain Dealer*, 1 December 1854.

41. *Detroit Free Press*, 2 December 1854; Telegrams, Forbes to Joy, 21, 21 December 1854, 11 January 1855, J. P.

7. THE TREACHEROUS EDITOR

1. Harvey to Joy, 22 September, 24 November 1853, J. P.; *Lake Superior Journal*, 16 July, 10 September 1853, 2 January, 17 June 1854.

2. Complaint of the Canal Company, 19 March 1855, Response of Defendant, 2 July 1855, Deposition of Harvey, 19 May 1856, *Canal Co.* v. *Brown*. In his statement Brown agreed to most of the facts of the case as presented by Harvey.

3. Signed agreement between Brooks and Brown, 5 November 1853, Plaintiff Exhibit No. 5, ibid.

4. Response of Defendant, 2 July 1855, Deposition of Ebenezer Warner, 13 August 1856, Plaintiff Exhibit No. 6, ibid.; Harvey to Joy, 24 November 1853, J. P.

5. Harvey to Whitwood, 5 January 1854, J. P.; had such a letter existed, Harvey would have offered it in *Canal Co.* v. *Brown*.

6. *Lake Superior Journal*, 17 May 1854.

7. Ibid., 27 May, 3 June 1854.

8. State of Michigan, *Documents Accompanying the Journal of the Senate, 1855* (Lansing, 1855), No. 19; George W. Knight, "History and Management of Land Grants for Education in the Northwest Territory," 1:38; Hibbard, *Public Land Policies*, p. 315.

9. State of Michigan, *Documents Accompanying the Journal of the Senate*, No. 19.

10. *Lake Superior Journal*, 27 May 1854; State of Michigan, *Michigan Joint Documents No. 5, 1873* (Lansing 1873).

11. *Lake Superior Journal*, 27 May, 3, 10 June 1854.

12. Ibid.

13. Churchill to Pruyn, 20 April 1854, C. P. I have not been able to locate a copy of the *Detroit Tribune* with the Fairbanks-Chapel article. However, its contents were reflected in the *Detroit Free Press*, 15 June 1854, and also in Brown's answer in *Lake Superior Journal*, 1 July 1854.

14. *Detroit Free Press*, 15 June 1854.

15. *Lake Superior Journal*, 1 July 1854.

16. Ibid., 12, 19 August 1854.

17. United States, Selection and Adjustment Lists, Archives.

18. *Lake Superior Journal*, 16, 23 September 1854.

19. Ibid., 9, 23, 30 September 1854; *Detroit Free Press*, 1 October 1854.

20. S. R. Wood to Joy, 24 March 1855, J. P.; Gara, *Woodman*, pp. 31–32; E. L. Briggs to Woodman, 19 March 1864, Michigan Pine Land Association Papers, Burton Historical Collection, Detroit Public Library, Detroit, Michigan; *Lake Superior Journal*, 24 July 1850, 8 October 1853; Minutes of an Offer to Sell the *Lake Superior Journal*, 5 October 1854, Burt Papers.

8. PRECARIOUS FINANCING

1. Pruyn to Joy, 23 June 1853; Pruyn to Stockholders, 6 September, 4 November 1853; Nichols to President and Directors, 15 September 1853, all in J. P.

2. A/C, unsigned, 1 September 1853; A/C, Harvey with Canal Company, 6 August 1853, both in S. P.

3. Brooks to Corning, 10 March, 9 November 1953; Telegrams, Brooks to Corning, 1, 29 September 1853; Davidson to Corning, 29 September 1853; Forbes to Seymour, copy to Corning, 29 September 1853; Churchill to Pruyn, 20 April 1854, all in C. P.; Notices from the Chicago and Aurora Railroad Company and the Illinois Central Railroad Company to Joy, numerous dates, 1853, J. P.

4. A/C, Detroit Land Office, 4 May 1854, J. P.; if there was any truth to Brown's charge of bribery of the Michigan authorities, the indication is here. There is no way that I can account for the sums $108,366 and $23,800 this early in the program.

5. A/C, Sault Office, 7 June 1854, S. P.

6. Brooks to Corning, 9, 19 January 1854; Telegram, Brooks to Corning, 19 January 1854, both in C. P.; Pruyn to Directors, 24 January, 3 February 1854, J. P.; Harvey to Fairbanks, 4 April, 17 June 1854, H. P.

7. Pruyn to Stockholders, 6 March, 25 May 1854, J. P.; Fairbanks to Corning, 7 June 1854, C. P.

8. Fairbanks to Corning, two letters and a sample note, 7 June 1854, C. P.; Brooks to Joy, 10 June 1854, J. P.

9. Pruyn to Joy, 15 July, 24 October 1854, J. P.; Fairbanks to Corning, 13 November 1854, C. P.; Pruyn to Directors, 19 August 1854, S. P.

10. Brooks to Corning, 12 July 1854, C. P.; Chandler, *Poor*, pp. 140–43. The dates of Poor's editorial charges were 28 October and 4 November 1854, and 7, 28 July, 11 August, and 1 September 1855.

11. Cancelled notes of H. Seymour dated 6 April, 26 July and 1 August 1854, S. P.

12. Unsigned letter to stockholders, 13 October 1854, S. P.

13. Pruyn to Stockholders, 2 November 1854; Fairbanks to Corning, 13, 20 November 1854, C. P.

9. THE FINAL PUSH

1. State of Michigan, "Report of John T. Clark, Chief Engineer," *Documents Accompanying the Journal of the Senate of Michigan, 1855* (Lansing, 1855), No. 11.

2. Ibid.

3. Ibid.

4. Ibid.

5. Telegrams, Brooks to Joy, 10 January, 7 February 1855, J. P.; Seymour to Corning, 6 February 1855, C. P.; State of Michigan, "Senate Document No. 19," 1855.

6. Seymour to Corning, 6 February 1855, C. P.; Pruyn to Joy, 19 January 1855, J. P.; Minutes of Directors Meeting, 24 January 1855, S. P.; Brooks to Corning, 19 January 1855; Pruyn to Directors, 17 January 1855, both in C. P.; Chandler to Bingham, 1 February 1855, Michigan Archives. The petition dated 23 January 1855 is also in the Michigan Archives.

7. Seymour to Corning, 6 February 1855, C. P.; Brooks to Fairbanks, 28 February, 16 April 1855, H. P.

8. Seymour to Corning, 6 February 1855; Brooks to Corning, 14 February 1855, both in C. P.; Brooks to Fairbanks, 13, 28 February 1855, H. P.

9. Seymour to Corning, 6 February 1855, C. P.; Brooks to Joy, 5 February 1855, J. P.

10. State of Michigan, *Laws of the State of Michigan, 1855* (Lansing, 1855), No. 91, pp. 195-96.

11. Ibid.; Brooks to Fairbanks, 28 February 1855, H. P.; Petition, 15 July 1855, Michigan Archives; *Lake Superior Journal*, 24 May 1855.

12. United States, "Selection and Adjustment Lists," Archives. The list for the Upper Peninsula alone is found in thirty-six ledger pages. Brooks to Fairbanks, 21 July 1854, 29 January 1855, H. P.

13. United States, "Lists"; Nichols, *Pierce*, pp. 250, 253, 416, 380.

14. Brooks to Fairbanks, 13 February, 14 April 1855, H. P.

15. Brooks to Fairbanks, 14, 16, 23 April 1855, H. P.; Howard to Bingham, 4 April 1855; Corning to Bingham, 16 April 1855; Brooks and Joy to Bingham, 28 April 1855; certified copy of assignment, 14 April 1855, all in Michigan Archives.

16. Complaint of the Canal Company, 19 March 1855; Deposition of Harvey, 19 May 1856, both in *Canal Co.* v. *Brown*; Theodore E. Burton, "The Improvement of Lake Channels," in *The Saint Marys Falls Canal*, Moore, p. 54; *Evening News* (Sault Ste. Marie, Michigan), 2, 3 August 1905.

17. Answer of Defendant, 2 July 1855, *Canal Co.* v. *Brown*.

18. Deposition of Joseph Kemp, 16 July 1856, and of Ebenezer Warner, 13 August 1856; Brown to Harvey, 19 November 1852, Plaintiff Exhibit "A," all in *Canal Co.* v. *Brown*.

19. Harvey to Seymour and Harvey to Corning, 1 January 1855; Harvey to Seymour, 1 February 1855, all in S. P.

20. Harvey to Seymour, 1 February 1855, S. P.

21. Canfield to McClelland, 1852, "Description of Canal," Archives.

22. Ibid.

23. Harvey to Seymour, 1 February 1855, the second of two letters of this date but marked for Seymour only; Harvey to Seymour, 3 February 1855, both in S. P.

24. Nichols to Brooks, 4 March 1855, H. P.

25. Brooks to Harvey, 9 March 1855, H. P.

26. Ibid.

27. Ibid.

28. Ibid.; Brooks to Fairbanks, 10, 17 March 1855, H. P.

29. Harvey to Fairbanks, 6 April 1855, H. P.

30. Harvey to Fairbanks, 6 April 1855, H. P.; Brooks to Fairbanks, 18, 23, 26 April, 2, 3 May 1855, H. P.; Pruyn to Directors, 7 May 1855, C. P. and J. P.; Fairbanks to Corning, 26 April, 3 May 1855, C. P.

31. Brooks to Fairbanks, 30 March 1855, H. P.; Brooks to Corning, 23 April, 20 May telegram and letter, 5 May 1855, C. P.

32. State of New York, *Report of State Engineer*, II, p. 1160; Corning, Joy, and Brooks to Bingham, McKinney, and Treadwell, 23 May 1855, S. P.

33. *Lake Superior Journal*, 24 May 1855; Corning, Joy, and Brooks to Bingham, McKinney and Treadwell, 23 May 1855, S. P.; Certifying Statement of Clark, 21 May 1855, both in S. P. Clark apparently certified on the word of McAlpine and predated the certificate.

34. Corning, Joy, and Brooks to Bingham, McKinney, and Treadwell, 23 May 1855, S. P.; Carlton, *Family History of Vermont*, p. 117.

35. Corning, Joy, and Brooks to Bingham, McKinney, and Treadwell, 23 May 1855, S. P.; my italics.

36. Seymour to Corning, 1 June 1855, C. P. There were at least three copies of the Corning, Joy, and Brooks letter in the Seymour collection and more scattered in other collections, indicating that a full publicity drive was ready. Brooks had gone into a minor panic after a fire had destroyed the Sault office, fearing that the same thing might happen in Detroit; Brooks to Corning, 28 February 1855, C. P.

37. Seymour to Corning, 1 July 1855, C. P.

38. Ibid. I have repeated this delightful crow of victory in its entirety in the Appendix.

39. Ibid. Quit Claim and Release of the Canal signed by Seymour and Brooks, 25 May 1855, Michigan Archives.

10. Counting the Cost and Operating the Canal

1. Moore, *Saint Marys Falls Canal*, pp. 125–26; *New York Daily Tribune*, 12 July 1847; State of Michigan, John Burt, "Report of the Superintendent of the St. Mary's Falls Ship Canal," *Joint Documents of the Legislature of the State of Michigan, 1857* (Detroit, 1857), p. 7.

2. Hibbard, *Public Land Policies*, pp. 29, 335.

3. A/C, Harvey, "Receipts and Disbursements for Six Months Ending January 1, 1856," S. P.

4. United States, "Detailed Drawings of Sault Canal," Archives; Shaw, *Erie Water West*, p. 207.

5. United States, Patent Office, Patent No. 65,054, 28 May 1867.

6. United States, Harry F. Hodges, *Notes on Mitering Lock Gates*, Professional Papers of the Corps of Engineers, United States Army, No. 26 (Washington, 1892). An excellent glossary of canal gate terms is found on pp. 7 and 8.

7. State of Michigan, "Report of Burt," p. 3; Philip P. Mason, ed., "The Operation of the Sault Canal, 1857," p. 75. For some reason the Michigan authorities did not publish the report of Superintendent Elisha Calkins for the year 1857. Mason's work made up for the deficiency.

8. *Washington Union* (Washington, D.C.), 12 April 1855; *Lake Superior Journal*, 24 May 1855; Harvey to Corning, 31 May 1855, C. P.

9. *Lake Superior Journal*, 24 May 1855; the same statistics were offered in Erastus Corning et al., *Report of the Directors of the St. Mary's Falls Ship Canal Company* (Detroit, 1858), Frontispiece.

10. Corning et al., *Report of the Directors*, Balance Sheet; Canfield to McClelland, "Estimate," Archives; Nichols to E. & T. Fairbanks Company, 9 December 1852, S. P.

11. Corning et al., *Report of the Directors*, Balance Sheet.

12. Ibid.

13. Ibid.; Neu, *Corning*, pp. 93–94.

14. State of Michigan, "Report of Burt," p. 4.

15. Moore, *Saint Marys Falls Canal*, pp. 125–26; *New York Daily Tribune*, 12 July 1847; State of Michigan, "Report of Burt," p. 7. Unfortunately Burt did not list the number of down passengers as an indication of the net gain in population in the Upper Peninsula.

16. State of Michigan, "Report of Burt," pp. 9–11.

17. Ibid., p. 12.

18. Mason, "Operation of Canal, 1857," p. 80; State of Michigan, "Report of the Superintendent of the St. Mary's Falls Ship Canal," *Joint Documents of the Legislature of the State of Michigan* (Detroit, years as indicated in text), including the following reports: "Elisha Calkins, 1858," p. 8; "Samuel P. Mead, 1859," p. 14, and "1860," p. 4; "George M. Brown, 1861," p. 15, and "1862," p. 13.

19. Mason, "Operation of Canal, 1857," p. 80; State of Michigan, "Report of Calkins, 1858," p. 8; "Report of Mead, 1859," p. 14, and "1860," p. 4; "Report of Brown, 1861," p. 15, and "1862," p. 13.

20. State of Michigan, "Report of Burt, 1857," p. 4.

21. State of Michigan, "Report of Calkins, 1858," pp. 4–5.

22. State of Michigan, "Report of Mead, 1860," pp. 1–3; "Report of Brown, 1861," p. 7.

23. State of Michigan, "Report of Brown, 1862," p. 10.

24. State of Michigan, "Report of Burt, 1857," p. 1; "Report of Mead, 1859," pp. 6–7.

25. State of Michigan, "Report of Mead, 1860," p. 10; undated deposition of Howard, Attorney General, Michigan Archives.

26. State of Michigan, "Report of Mead, 1859," p. 7.

27. Ibid., pp. 7–8.

28. State of Michigan, *Joint Documents of the State of Michigan, 1877*, 4 vols. (Lansing, 1877), 3:8–9; Utley and Cutcheon, *Michigan*, 3:400.

29. State of Michigan, "Report of Brown, 1861," pp. 6–7; "1862," pp. 5–7; *Joint Documents of the State of Michigan, 1864* (Detroit, 1864), No. 14.

30. State of Michigan, "Report of Calkins, 1858," pp. 1–2; "Report of Mead, 1859," p. 2; "1860," p. 6; "Report of Brown, 1861," p. 4.

11. The Canal Company Lands

1. Anthony S. Wax, "Calumet and Hecla Copper Mines: An Episode in the Economic Development of Michigan," pp. 11–12; *Cleveland Daily Herald*, 11 August 1851; United States, *Senate Executive Documents*, 31st Cong., 1st Sess., III, No. 1, pp. 760–65; *Senate Executive Documents*, 29th Cong., 1st Sess., VII, No. 357, p. 10; State of Michigan, *Documents Accompanying the Journal of the House of Representatives of the State of Michigan, 1841* (Detroit, 1841), p. 519; Utley and Cutcheon, *Michigan*, pp. 329–30. See maps, "Copper Claims on the Keweenaw Peninsula, 3 and 4," this chapter.

2. Mentor L. Williams, "Horace Greeley and Michigan Copper," p. 120; *New York Daily Tribune*, 12 July 1847; Greeley, *Recollections*, p. 244; *Hunt's Merchants' Magazine* 8 (April 1843): 385, 11 (November 1844): 482, 14 (May 1846): 439–43.

3. St. John, *Description of Superior Country*, p. 93; Lanman, *A Summer in the Wilderness*, pp. 152–55.

4. *L. S. N. & M. J.*, 11 July 1846; *Hunt's Merchants' Magazine* 25 (August 1851): 254.

5. Gara, *Woodman*, p. 84.

6. Harvey to Brown, 10 April 1853, Plaintiff Exhibit No. 2, *Canal Co.* v. *Brown*.

7. United States, *House Executive Documents*, 31st Cong., 1st Sess., IX, No. 69, pp. 146–51.

8. United States, *Senate Executive Documents*, 31st Cong., 1st Sess., III, No. 1, pp. 387, 612–15, 760–65.

9. State of Michigan, *Joint Documents of the Legislature of the State of Michigan, 1850* (Detroit, 1850), pp. 50–59.

10. Harvey to Brown, 10 April 1853, Plaintiff Exhibit No. 2, *Canal Co.* v. *Brown*; United States, "Geological Map of the District between Keweenaw Bay and the Chocolay River, Lake Superior, Michigan," *Senate Executive Documents*, 31st Cong., 1st Sess., III, No. 1.

11. A/C, Brown with Canal Company, Plaintiff Exhibit No. 6, *Canal Co.* v. *Brown*; United States, *House Executive Documents*, 31st Cong., 1st Sess., IX, No. 69, pp. 146–51.

12. Commissions to Frost and Whitwood signed by Parsons, "Falls of St. Mary's River," Archives; Brooks to Fairbanks, 24 March 1854, H. P.

13. Brooks to Porter, 2 June 1853; Harvey to Joy, 22 September 1853, both in J. P.

14. Brooks to Fairbanks, 24 March, 20 April 1854, H. P.; George S. Frost, *Pine Lands in the State of Michigan with Lumber Statistics and Other Valuable Information Concerning the Pine Lands of the Saint Mary's Falls Ship Canal Company*, pp. 3–4.

15. "Falls of St. Mary's River," Archives; C. A. Trowbridge to Joy, 23 May 1855, J. P.

16. "Falls of the St. Mary's River," Archives; Frost's error was detected only through use of an electronic calculator, the tapes of which were proofread twice.

17. Frost, *Pine Lands*, pp. 6–8.

18. Ibid.

19. See map, "Copper Claims on the Keweenaw Peninsula, 3," this chapter.

20. The figures in parentheses indicate the tons of copper produced and the company dividends paid through 1925 as extracted from Butler and Burbank, *Copper Deposits in Michigan*. See maps, "Copper Claims on the Keweenaw Peninsula," 1 and 3, this chapter.

21. See map, "Copper Claims on the Keweenaw Peninsula, 3," this chapter.

22. Ibid.; George R. Agassiz, ed., *The Letters and Recollections of Alexander Agassiz*, pp. 54–57; Wax, "Calumet and Hecla," pp. 14–16. This was by no means the full extent of the Calumet and Hecla holdings; see maps, "Copper Claims on the Keweenaw Peninsula," 3 and 4, this chapter.

23. See maps, "Copper Claims on the Keweenaw Peninsula," 4 and 5, this chapter.

24. See map, "Copper Claims on the Keweenaw Peninsula, 1," this chapter.

25. See map, "Iron Ore Claims in Marquette County," this chapter.

26. Ibid.

27. Ibid.; Moore, *Saint Marys Falls Canal*, p. 31.

28. See map, "Lumber Claims in Delta County and Southern Schoolcraft County," this chapter.

29. See maps, "Lumber Claims in Alger County and Northern Schoolcraft County," and "Lumber Claims in Mackinac County," this chapter.

30. "Falls of St. Mary's River," Archives.

12. LAND FOR SALE

1. Cochran, *Railroad Leaders*, pp. 42, 128–29; Harvey to Fairbanks, 4 July 1855, H. P.; William B. Gates, Jr., *Michigan Copper and Boston Dollars*, p. 10. For a complete treatment of eastern railroad investors' strategies, see Arthur M. Johnson and Barry E. Supple, *Boston Capitalists and Western Railroads*.

2. Brooks to Corning, 7, 23, 28 July, 15 August, 21, 26 September 1855; Fairbanks to Corning, 7 August 1855, all in C. P.; Brooks to Fairbanks, 9 January 1854, H. P.

3. Frost to Corning, 11 July, 17, 24 August 1855; Fairbanks to Corning, 7 August 1855; Brooks to Corning, 26 September 1855, all in C. P.; Harvey to Seymour, 1 January 1856, S. P.

4. Harvey to Fairbanks, 1 January 1856, H. P.; Harvey to Seymour, 1 January 1856, S. P.

5. Harvey to Fairbanks, 1 January 1856, H. P.; Harvey to Seymour, 1 January 1856, S. P.

6. Hereafter cited as the Mineral Company.

7. The best presentation of the sale of mineral lands in the Upper Peninsula is in Irene D. Neu, "The Mineral Lands of the Saint Mary's Falls Ship Canal," especially pp. 175–82. This work contains some revisions of Neu, *Corning*, p. 153. See also Butler and Burbank, *Copper Deposits of Michigan*, p. 77; State of Michigan, T. B. Brooks, "Iron Bearing Rocks," *Geological Survey of Michigan: Upper Peninsula 1869–1873*, vol. 1, pt. 1, p. 25.

8. Butler and Burbank, *Copper Deposits of Michigan*, pp. 79, 82; Gates, "Michigan Copper," p. 162.

9. Neu, *Corning*, pp. 153–54; State of Michigan, *Geological Survey*, vol. 1, pt. 1, p. 24; Agassiz to Quincy Shaw, December (?), 1867, as cited in *Agassiz*, ed. G. R. Agassiz, p. 79.

10. Neu, "The Mineral Lands," pp. 182–83.

11. Frost, *Pine Lands*, p. 6; Corning et al., *Report of Directors, 1858*.

12. Forbes to Nassau W. Senior, as cited in *Forbes*, ed. Hughes, 1:257; Gara, *Woodman*, pp. 153–56; *New York Daily Tribune*, 7 May 1862.

13. Gara, *Woodman*, pp. 153–56.

14. Ibid.

15. Neu, *Corning*, pp. 154–55; "Articles of Association," Michigan Pine Lands Association Papers, Burton Historical Collection; Cochran, *Railroad Leaders*, p. 37.

16. Neu, *Corning*, pp. 156–57; Gara, *Woodman*, pp. 25, 41, 156–59.

17. Neu estimated that Corning alone purchased about 100,000 acres; Neu, *Corning*, p. 157. Deed of sale of land by Fairbanks as president, 1 October 1863, Mears Papers, Burton Historical Collection.

18. "Articles of Association," Michigan Pine Lands Association, Burton Historical Collection; Gara, *Woodman*, p. 172.

19. "Articles of Association," Michigan Pine Lands Association, Burton Historical Collection; Gara, *Woodman*, p. 172.

20. "Articles of Association," Michigan Pine Land Association, Burton Historical Collection; Gara, *Woodman*, p. 172.

21. Mason, "Report of Calkins," p. 76; Albert S. French to Woodman, 21 October 1864, Michigan Pine Lands Association Papers, Burton Historical Collection; Gara, *Woodman*, p. 143.

22. Gara, *Woodman*, p. 143; Neu, *Corning*, pp. 189, 159. Corning's land books were not preserved.

23. Butler and Burbank, *Copper Deposits of Michigan*, pp. 67–68, 74.

EPILOGUE

1. Robert V. Bruce, *Lincoln and the Tools of War* (New York, 1956), pp. 42–43.
2. Madison Kuhn, *Michigan State: The First Hundred Years* (Chicago, 1955), pp. 9, 72–75.

Bibliography

MANUSCRIPT COLLECTIONS

Burt Papers, J. M. Longyear Research Library, Marquette County Historical Society, Marquette, Michigan.

Charles Thompson Harvey Papers, J. M. Longyear Research Library, Marquette County Historical Society, Marquette, Michigan.

Erastus Corning Papers, Albany Institute of History and Art, Albany, New York.

Horatio Seymour Collection, Collection of Regional History, Cornell University, Ithaca, New York.

James F. Joy Papers, Burton Historical Collection, Detroit Public Library, Detroit, Michigan.

Mears Papers, Burton Historical Collection, Detroit Public Library, Detroit, Michigan.

Michigan Pine Lands Association Papers, Burton Historical Collection, Detroit Public Library, Detroit, Michigan.

St. Mary's Falls Ship Canal Company v. *Joseph V. Brown*, Wayne County Circuit Court, Chancery No. 608, Old County Building, Detroit, Michigan.

FEDERAL SOURCES—NATIONAL ARCHIVES, WASHINGTON, D. C.

Bureau of Land Management, "Falls of the Saint Mary's River," Record Group 49.

Office of the Adjutant General, Post Returns, Record Group 94.

Office of the Chief of Engineers, Reports of Army Topographical Engineers, Record Group 77.

Office of the Chief of Engineers, Survey of Fort Brady, Sault Ste. Marie, Record Group 77.

Records of the General Land Office, Selection and Adjustment Lists, 1850–1921, Division F, Record Group 49.

FEDERAL DOCUMENTS—MISCELLANEOUS

Acts Passed at the First Session of the Eighteenth Congress of the United States. Washington, 1824.

Army Meteorological Register, 1843–1854. Washington, 1855.

Biographical Directory of the American Congress, 1774–1961. Washington, 1961.

Commissioner of Indian Affairs. *Treaties between the United States of America and the Several Indian Tribes*. Washington, 1837.

Congressional Directory for the First Session of the Thirty Second Congress. Washington, 1852.

Congressional Globe.

Department of Interior. B. S. Butler and W. B. Burbank. *The Copper Deposits of Michigan*. Professional Paper 144. Washington, 1929.

Engineering Department. "Detailed Drawings of St. Mary's Falls Canal and Locks, Michigan." Washington, 1882–84.

House of Representatives Executive Documents.

Patent Office. Patent No. 65, 054.

Professional Papers of the Corps of Engineers. Harry F. Hodges. *Notes on Mitering of Lock Gates*. No. 26. Washington, 1892.

Senate Documents. Israel Andrews. "Report on the Trade and Commerce of the British North American Colonies and the Trade of the Great Lakes and Rivers." 32d Cong., 1st Sess. 12:220–22.

Senate Executive Documents.

Seventh Census of the United States, 1850. Washington, 1853.

Statutes at Large and Treaties of the United States of America: From December 1, 1845 to March 3, 1851. Vol. 9. Boston, 1851. *From December 1, 1851 to March 3, 1855*. Vol. 10. Boston, 1855.

STATE DOCUMENTS, MICHIGAN

Acts of the Legislature of the State of Michigan Passed at the Regular Session of 1853. Lansing, 1853.

Census and Statistics of the State of Michigan, May, 1854. Lansing, 1854.

Documents Accompanying the Journal of the House of Representatives of the State of Michigan. Lansing and Detroit.

Documents Accompanying the Journal of the Senate of the State of Michigan. Lansing and Detroit.

Geological Survey of Michigan: Upper Peninsula 1869–1873. New York and Lansing, 1873–1903.

Joint Documents of the Legislature of the State of Michigan. Detroit.

Joint Documents of the State of Michigan. Lansing.

Journal of the House of Representatives of the State of Michigan. Lansing.

Journal of the Senate of the State of Michigan. Lansing.

STATE DOCUMENTS—MISCELLANEOUS

State of Indiana. *Journal of the Indiana State Senate: Thirty Sixth Session, 1851–1852*. Indianapolis, 1852.

State of New York. *Documents of the Assembly of the State of New York, 1843*. Albany, 1843.

———. Election and Laws Bureau, Office of the Secretary of the State of New York. Albany, New York.

———. *Journal of the Senate of the State of New York: Seventy Fifth Session, 1852*. Albany, 1852.

———. William J. McAlpine. "Reports and Estimates for a Ship Canal and Basin from Albany to New Baltimore." *New York Miscellaneous Pamphlets*. Vol. 1. Albany, New York.

———. *Supplement to the Annual Report of the State Engineer and Surveyor of the State of New York*. 2 vols. Albany, 1906.

State of Ohio. *Documents, Messages, and Other Communications Made to the Forty First General Assembly of the State of Ohio*. Columbus, 1853.

State of Vermont. *Journal of the House of Representatives of the State of Vermont, 1855*. Montpelier, 1855.

NEWSPAPERS

Albany Evening Journal (Albany, New York).
Daily Albany Argus (Albany, New York).
Daily Evening Star (Washington, D.C.).
Daily Herald (Cleveland, Ohio).
Daily Plain Dealer (Cleveland, Ohio).
Detroit Daily Advertiser (Detroit, Michigan).
Detroit Free Press (Detroit, Michigan).
Evening News (Sault Ste. Marie, Michigan).
Lake Superior Journal (Sault Ste. Marie and Detroit, Michigan).
Lake Superior News and Miners' Journal (Copper Harbor, Michigan).
Lake Superior News and Mining Journal (Sault Ste. Marie, Michigan).
Louisville Courier (Louisville, Kentucky).
Merchants' Magazine and Commercial Review (New York, New York).
New York Daily Tribune (New York, New York).
New York Weekly Tribune (New York, New York).
Niles National Register (Baltimore, Maryland).
Washington Union (Washington, D.C.).
Washtenaw Whig (Ann Arbor, Michigan).

OTHER SOURCES

Agassiz, George R., ed. *The Letters and Recollections of Alexander Agassiz*. London, 1913.

Agassiz, Louis. *Lake Superior: Its Physical Character, Vegetation, and Animals . . . With a Narrative of the Tour by J. Elliot Cabot*. Boston, 1850.

Angle, Paul M., ed. "The Western Trip of Philip Hone." *Journal of the Illinois State Historical Society* 38(1945):277–94.

Bald, Frederick Clever. *Michigan in Four Centuries*. New York, 1954.

Barnard, F. A., comp. *American Biographical History of Eminent and Self-Made Men*. Michigan volume. Cincinnati, 1878.

Barton, James L. *Lake Commerce, Letter to the Hon. Robert McClelland*. Buffalo, 1846.

Beckman, Peter. "James F. Joy and the Western Railroads." MS in the Burton Historical Collection, Detroit Public Library, Detroit, Michigan.

Beeson, Lewis, and Victor F. Lemmer. *The Effects of the Civil War on Mining in Michigan*. Lansing, 1966.

Bingham, S. D., comp. *Early History of Michigan with Biographies*. Lansing, 1888.

Blake, Nelson Manfred. *Water for the Cities*. Syracuse, 1956.

Bradish, Alvah. *Memoir of Douglass Houghton*. Detroit, 1889.

Cain, Marvin R. *Lincoln's Attorney General: Edward Bates of Missouri*. Columbia, Mo., 1965.

Calhoun, Daniel H. *American Civil Engineers*. Cambridge, Mass., 1960.

Carlton, Hiram, comp. *Genealogical and Family History of the State of Vermont*. New York. 1903.

Catton, Bruce, *Michigan: A Bicentennial History*. New York, 1976.

Chandler, Alfred D., Jr. *Henry Varnum Poor: Business Editor, Analyst, and Reformer*. Cambridge, Mass., 1956.

_____. "The Railroads: Pioneers in Modern Corporate Management." *Business History Review* 39 (1965):16–40.

de Charlevoix, P. *Journal d'un voyage fait far ordre du roi dans l'Amerique septentrionale*. 3 vols. Paris, 1744.

Clawson, Marion, and Burnell Held. *The Federal Lands: Their Use and Management*. Baltimore, 1957.

Cochran, Thomas C. *Railroad Leaders, 1845–1890*. Cambridge, Mass., 1953.

Coyle, David C. *Conservation*. New Brunswick, N.J., 1957.

Cullum, George W., comp. *Biographical Register of the Officers and Graduates of the United States Military Academy*. 5 vols. Boston, 1891–1901.

Decker, Leslie E. *Railroads, Lands, and Politics*. Providence, R.I., 1964.

Dorfman, Joseph. *The Economic Mind in American Civilization. 1606–1865*. 2 vols. New York, 1953.

Dunbar, Willis Frederick. *Michigan through the Centuries*. 4 vols. New York, 1955.

Elazar, Daniel J. "Gubernatorial Power and the Illinois and Michigan Canal." *Journal of the Illinois State Historical Society* 23 (1965):396–423.

Ellet, Elizabeth F. *Summer Rambles in the West*. New York, 1853.

Fatout, Paul. "Canal Agitation at Ohio Falls." *Indiana Magazine of History* 57 (December 1961):279–309.

Fennimore, Jean J. "Austin Blair: Political Idealist, 1845–1860." *Michigan History* 48 (1964):130–66.

Fergus, Robert, comp. "Chicago River and Harbor Convention." *Fergus Historical Series No. 18*. Chicago, 1882.

Fowle, Otto. *Sault Ste. Marie and Its Great Waterway*. New York, 1925.

Franklin, John Hope. "The Southern Expansionists of 1846." *Journal of Southern History* 25 (1959):323–38.

Frost, George S. *Pine Lands in the State of Michigan with Lumber Statistics, and Other Valuable Information Concerning the Pine Lands of the St. Mary's Falls Ship Canal Company*. Detroit, 1857.

Gara, Larry. *Westernized Yankee: The Story of Cyrus Woodman*. Madison, Wis., 1956.

Gates, William B., Jr. *Michigan Copper and Boston Dollars*. Cambridge, Mass., 1951.

Goodrich, Carter, et al. *Canals and American Economic Development*. New York, 1961.

———. "American Development Policy: The Case of Internal Improvements." In *American History: Recent Interpretations*, ed. Abraham Eisenstadt. Vol. 1, pp. 349–61. New York, 1962.

———. *Government Promotion of American Canals and Railroads, 1800–1890*. New York, 1960.

———. "The Revulsion against Internal Improvements." *Journal of Economic History* 10 (November 1950):145–69.

Greeley, Horace. *Recollections of a Busy Life*. New York, 1868.

Hamilton, Holman. *Zachary Taylor*. 2 vols. New York, 1951.

Harlow, Alvin. *The Road of the Century*. New York, 1947.

Hatcher, Harlan. *A Century of Iron and Men*. New York, 1950.

Hibbard, Benjamin H. *A History of the Public Land Policies*. New York, 1924.

Hill, Forest S. *Roads, Rails, and Waterways: The Army Engineers and Early Transportation*. Norman, Okla., 1957.

Horberg, Leland, and Richard C. Anderson. "Bedrock Topology and Pleistocene Glacial Lobes in Central United States." *Journal of Geology* 64 (1956):102–16.

Hough, Jack L. *Geology of the Great Lakes.* Urbana, Ill., 1958.

Hughes, Sarah Forbes, ed. *Letters and Recollections of John Murray Forbes.* 2 vols. Boston, 1899.

Hybels, Robert James. "The Lake Superior Copper Fever, 1841–1847." *Michigan History* 34 (June, September, December 1949):97–119, 224–44, 309–26.

Johnson, Arthur M., and Barry E. Supple. *Boston Capitalists and Western Railroads.* Cambridge, Mass., 1967.

Knight, George W. "History and Management of Land Grants for Education in the Northwest Territory." In *Papers of the American Historical Association.* 5 vols. New York, 1885. 1:7–173.

Lanman, Charles. *A Summer in the Wilderness, Embracing a Canoe Voyage up the Mississippi and around Lake Superior.* New York, 1847.

"Life History of Charles Thompson Harvey." Author unknown but probably Sarah Van Eps Harvey (Mrs. Charles Thompson Harvey), in the Charles Thompson Harvey papers, J. M. Longyear Research Library, Marquette County Historical Society, Marquette, Michigan.

Lurie, Edward. *Louis Agassiz: A Life in Science.* Chicago, 1960.

McLaughlin, Andrew C. *Lewis Cass.* New York, 1891.

Mason, Philip P., ed. "The Operation of the Sault Canal, 1857." *Michigan History* 39 (1955):69–80.

Michigan Historical Commission, comp. *Michigan Biographies.* 2 vols. Lansing, 1924.

Michigan Pioneer and Historical Society, comp. *Michigan Pioneer and Historical Collection.* 40 vols. Lansing, 1874–1929.

Moore, Charles, ed. *Saint Marys Falls Canal Semicentennial, 1905.* Detroit, 1907.

Mushkat, Jerome. "Mineral and Timber Prospects in Upper Michigan: The 1858 Diary of John V. L. Pruyn." *Inland Seas* 30 (1974):84–89.

Neu, Irene D. "The Building of the Sault Canal: 1852–1855." *Mississippi Valley Historical Review* 40 (1953):25–46.

_____. *Erastus Corning: Merchant and Financier.* Ithaca, N. Y., 1960.

_____. "The Mineral Lands of the St. Mary's Falls Ship Canal Company." In *The Frontier in American Development: Essays in Honor of Paul Wallace Gates*, ed. David M. Ellis, pp. 162–91. Ithaca, N. Y., 1969.

Nevins, Allen, ed. *The Diary of Philip Hone.* New York, 1936.

Nichols, Roy F. *Franklin Pierce.* Philadelphia, 1958.

Norton, Clark F. "Early Movement for St. Mary's Falls Ship Canal." *Michigan History* 39 (1955):257–80.

Parks, Robert J. *Democracy's Railroads: Public Enterprise in Jacksonian Michigan.* Port Washington, N. Y., 1967.

Pearson, Henry Greenleafe. *An American Railroad Builder, John Murray Forbes.* New York, 1911.

Poor, Henry V. *History of the Railroads and Canals of the United States of America.* New York, 1860.

Poore, Ben Perley, comp. *The Federal and State Constitutions, Colonial Charters, and Other Organic Laws of the United States.* 2 vols. Washington, 1877.

Porter, Kirk H., and Donald Bruce Johnson, comps. *National Party Platforms, 1840–1960.* Urbana, Ill., 1961.

Prucha, Francis Paul. *A Guide to the Military Posts of the United States.* Madison, Wis., 1964.

Quaife, Milo M., ed. *Alexander Henry's Travels and Adventures in the Years 1760–1776.* Chicago, 1921.

Rae, John Bell. "Federal Land Grants in Aid of Canals." *Journal of Economic History* 4 (1944):167–77.

Rankin, Ernest H. "Canalside Superintendent." *Inland Seas* 31 (1965):103–14.

Ransom, Roger L. "Public Canal Investment and the Opening of the Old Northwest." In *Essays in Nineteenth Century Economic History,* ed. David C. Klingaman and Richard R. Vedder. Athens, Ohio, 1976.

Rayback, Robert J. *Millard Fillmore: Biography of a President.* Buffalo, 1959.

Richardson, James D., comp. *A Compilation of the Messages and Papers of the Presidents of the United States, 1789–1897.* 10 vols. Washington, 1897.

Rivot, Louis Adouard. *Voyage au Lac Superieur.* Paris, 1855.

Robbins, Roy M. *Our Landed Heritage.* Princeton, 1942.

Rosenberg, Charles E. *The Cholera Years.* Chicago, 1962.

St. John, John R. *A True Description of the Lake Superior Country.* New York, 1846.

Scheiber, Harry N. *Ohio Canal Era: A Case Study of Government and the Economy, 1820–1861.* Athens, Ohio, 1969.

Shaw, Ronald E. *Erie Water West: A History of the Erie Canal, 1792–1854.* Lexington, Ky., 1966.

Silbey, Joel H. "The Civil War Synthesis in American Political History." *Civil War History* 10 (June 1964):130–40.

_____. "The Slavery Extension Controversy and Illinois Congressmen." *Journal of the Illinois State Historical Society* 58 (1965):378–95.

Steel, Edward M., Jr. *T. Butler King of Georgia.* Athens, Ga., 1964.

Stevens, Frank Walker. *The Beginnings of the New York Central Railroad.* New York, 1926.

Stevens, Walter W. "Lewis Cass and the Presidency." *Michigan History* 49 (June 1965):123–34.

Thwaites, Reuben Gold, ed. *The Jesuit Relations and Allied Documents*. 73 vols. Cleveland, 1896–1901.

Trescott, Paul B. "The Louisville and Portland Canal Company, 1825–1874." *Mississippi Valley Historical Review* 44 (March 1958):686–708.

Tuckerman, Bayard, ed. *The Diary of Philip Hone*. 2 vols. New York, 1889.

Utley, Henry M., and Byron M. Cutcheon. *Michigan as a Province, Territory, and State*. 4 vols. New York, 1906.

Van Deusen, Glyndon G. *Horace Greeley: Nineteenth Century Crusader*. Philadelphia, 1953.

_____. *Thurlow Weed: Wizard of the Lobby*. Boston, 1947.

Van Hise, Charles R. *The Conservation of Natural Resources in the United States*. New York, 1914.

_____, and Charles Kenneth Leith. *The Geology of the Lake Superior Region*. Washington, 1911.

Wax, Anthony S. "Calumet and Hecla Copper Mines: An Episode in the Economic Development of Michigan." *Michigan History* 16 (Winter 1932):5–41.

Williams, Mentor L. "The Background of the Chicago River and Harbor Convention, 1847." *Mid-America* 30 (October 1948), 219–32.

_____. "The Chicago River and Harbor Convention, 1847." *Mississippi Valley Historical Review* 35 (March 1949):607–26.

_____. "Horace Greeley and Michigan Copper." *Michigan History* 34 (June 1950):120–32.

Williams, Ralph D. *The Honorable Peter White: A Biographical Sketch of the Lake Superior Iron Country*. Cleveland, 1907.

Wiltse, Charles M. *John C. Calhoun, Sectionalist, 1840–1850*. New York, 1951.

Woodford, Frank B. *Lewis Cass*. New Brunswick, N. J., 1950.

Young, William T. *The Life of Lewis Cass*. Detroit, 1852.

Index

DATE DUE	
	MP 728